GHOST HUNTER
GAURAV TIWARI

Abhirup Dhar is a Kolkata-born, bestselling author of books such as, *Once Again…With Love!, Stories Are Magical, Hold That Breath!, The Belvoirbrooke Haunting, Hold That Breath 2* and *Ghost Hunter, Gaurav Tiwari: The Life and Legacy of India's Foremost Paranormal Investigator.* Dhar's writing has been endorsed by the renowned film-makers Vikram Bhatt and Sunil Bohra, who also acquired the screen rights for *Ghost Hunter, Gaurav Tiwari.* Dhar also writes movie scripts with reputed film-makers. A recipient of various awards and honours, Dhar has been called by *Mid-Day* as the most acclaimed name in Indian horror writing.

Indian Paranormal Society (IPS) was founded by Gaurav Tiwari in 2009. It has been a pioneer in metaphysical/anomalous research around the globe, especially in India. The collective gained popularity in the field of paranormal research because of the investigations they handled by travelling to different parts of the country. IPS aims to shun myths and superstitions about the paranormal through logical evaluation, critical thinking and applying principles of forensic science. IPS has helped thousands get rid of their fear of the unknown by spreading awareness about this field.

You can reach Indian Paranormal Society at:
Website: https://indianparanormalsociety.in/
E-mail: indianparanormalsociety@gmail.com
Facebook: www.facebook.com/indianparanormalsociety
YouTube: www.youtube.com/gripindia
Twitter: https://twitter.com/GRIPOfficial02?s=09
Instagram: https://www.instagram.com/indian_paranormal_society0209/

Also by the author

Hauntings: Stories Based on Actual

Paranormal Investigations

GHOST HUNTER
GAURAV TIWARI

The Life and Legacy of India's Foremost
Paranormal Investigator

ABHIRUP DHAR *and*
INDIAN PARANORMAL SOCIETY

RUPA

Published by
Rupa Publications India Pvt. Ltd 2023
7/16, Ansari Road, Daryaganj
New Delhi 110002

Sales centres:
Prayagraj Bengaluru Chennai
Hyderabad Jaipur Kathmandu
Kolkata Mumbai

First published by Westland Publications Private Limited 2021

P-ISBN: 978-93-5520-966-5
E-ISBN: 978-93-5520-972-6

First impression 2023

10 9 8 7 6 5 4 3 2 1

Printed in India

Dedicated to the memory of Gaurav Tiwari, beloved son, friend and brother and CEO/founder of the Indian Paranormal Society

O Captain! my Captain! our fearful trip is done,
The ship has weather'd every rack, the prize we sought
   is won,
The port is near, the bells I hear, the people all exulting,
While follow eyes the steady keel, the vessel grim and daring;
       But O heart! heart! heart!
       O the bleeding drops of red,
       Where on the deck my Captain lies,
       Fallen cold and dead.

O Captain! my Captain! rise up and hear the bells;
Rise up—for you the flag is flung—for you the bugle trills,
For you bouquets and ribbon'd wreaths—for you the
   shores a-crowding,
For you they call, the swaying mass, their eager faces turning;
       Here Captain! dear father!
       This arm beneath your head!
       It is some dream that on the deck,
       You've fallen cold and dead.

My Captain does not answer, his lips are pale and still,
My father does not feel my arm, he has no pulse nor will,
The ship is anchor'd safe and sound, its voyage closed
   and done,
From fearful trip the victor ship comes in with object won;
       Exult O shores, and ring O bells!
       But I with mournful tread,
       Walk the deck my Captain lies,
       Fallen cold and dead.

– O Captain! my Captain
Walt Whitman

CONTENTS

ACKNOWLEDGEMENTS

Reverend Gaurav Tiwari's life was exemplary in the way he transfigured his true passion into a full-time profession. He dedicated his life to educating people about things that are usually either brushed away with the excuse that they aren't supposed to be discussed or acknowledged, or considered to be a by-product of a fanciful mind.

This book perfectly captures his journey, and our experiences through the years we spent with him. It also reflects the knowledge he passed on to us. We hope readers enjoy this book as much as we did working on it. This has been an emotional rollercoaster for us as a team and as individuals. Each of us had our special connection with Gaurav Tiwari, and only we know what it feels like to be without our leader, our mentor and our captain. If he had been here today, he would have stood tall and proud. This is his stage, his life and we only hope that we, as his team members, have done justice to his name and legacy.

We extend our warmest regards to everyone who contributed to this book by narrating their experiences with Gaurav Tiwari. This includes Allen Tiller, Robb Demarest, Ian Lawman, Ray Jorden, Rayleen Kable from the *Haunting: Australia* team, Flame Productions, SyFy Australia, Really TV UK, Mama Owl Paranormal Team, Dr Doug Kelley (founder/president of Paranexus Anomalous Research Association and The Institute of Metaphysical Humanistic Science). We also thank Dr Nandini Sinha Kapur for her continuous support and guidance and for sharing her personal experiences with Gaurav Tiwari. We're also thankful to his family, friends and supporters who stood by us and propped up our team, work and every project that we worked on, regardless of Gaurav Tiwari's absence.

Last but not the least, we'd like to thank Abhirup Dhar for brilliantly bringing our words to life in the form of a narrative. Also, our literary agent Suhail Mathur for connecting us to some of the best people in the publishing and film industries, and helping us spread the word of our work to millions of people across the country.

– **Members of the Indian Paranormal Society**
(Meghna Porwal, Waqar Raj, Rith Deb,
Mohan Kattimani, Siddharth Bantval)

Thank you, dear readers, book reviewers and litterateurs for being there and for your valuable feedback. I believe one should never stop learning and that there is always scope for improvement, no matter how good things turn out. I sincerely hope you have a good time reading this labour of love too.

Mom and Dad, I feel happy to make both of you proud

with whatever I have been doing. All the sacrifices you made are always realised and remembered.

My lovely wife Chandrani has been with me through thick and thin. Thank you for understanding I'm a dreamer and always aspired to be different ... well, just a little. Your support while I try to weave stories and pen them down is an important part of my writing process.

My good friends and well-wishers, including relatives, cheers to us. I'd love to mention all your names but I'm mostly asked to keep this space brief! Yes, this one's for all of you too. Count yourselves in here, please, my friends from the writing fraternity!

I always keep mentioning in my talks, interviews and articles that I'm a proud Hermonite. Those ten beautiful years in Mount Hermon School (Darjeeling) are fondly recalled and I have vivid memories of my growing up years. *Non Scholae Sed Vitae Discimus*—Not for school but for life we learn. Thank you, dear teachers.

Thank you, Westland Publications, for having faith in this important book.

I'd like to thank my literary agent Suhail Mathur of The Book Bakers for his confidence in this project right from the start and his support throughout. His inputs and suggestions have bettered the writing. He made sure to leave no stone unturned to get us the best for this book and also connect us to accomplished people in the film industry for the screen adaptation.

Meghna Porwal, Siddharth Bantval, Waqar Raj, Rith Deb, Mohan Kattimani from the Indian Paranormal Society, Allen Tiller, Robb Demarest, Ian Lawman, Ray

Jorden, Rayleen Kable from *Haunting: Australia* and Dr Doug Kelley have been very cooperative. I know how special this book is to all of them as so many emotions are attached to Reverend Gaurav Tiwari.

It has been a life-altering experience for me, working on this book. Here's hoping you enjoy the very interesting true accounts of him and his dynamic and passionate team, living his dream and vision. The pioneers of paranormal investigation in India deserve the best and this book is an attempt to bring to you their journey.

Sunil Bohra, Prabhleen Kaur, Jai Mehta, Saurav Dey and the entire team—thank you for taking this book to the screen in order to reach out to a wider audience.

– Abhirup Dhar

WHO IS REVEREND GAURAV TIWARI?

We say 'is' because he is still alive in our hearts and minds.

Reverend Gaurav Tiwari (2 September 1984 – 7 July 2016) is the CEO and founder of the Indian Paranormal Society, and the director of G.R.I.P. (Ghost Research and Investigators of the Paranormal) Academy.[1] His aspiration to become a certified commercial pilot took him to Florida, where he successfully completed the training program and was presented with a commercial pilot licence. During his stay in Florida, he lived with a few of his batchmates from flying school in a rental apartment. Here, he experienced things that he did not have an explanation for. At the time, he neither believed in ghosts nor was he aware of the paranormal. However, those experiences made him research

---

[1] The Indian Paranomal Society is a trust under which there are different teams that specialise in various researches: UFOs, the metaphysical, crypto-zoologists, etc. As time progressed, all the teams were merged under G.R.I.P. Later, G.R.I.P. became synonymous with IPS. It's a model that is common in the West too. For example, the ParaNexus Anomalous Research Association, an institution dedicated to metaphysical research in Florida, has its own investigation wing called the SPIRIT team.

this topic and later join ParaNexus Anomalous Research Association to earn his degree in metaphysical/paranormal research. Post his return to India in 2009, he established India's first professional paranormal team and named it Indian Paranormal Society. Over the years, he featured on different television shows in India, promoting paranormal/ metaphysical research while at the same time ensuring that the element of entertainment wasn't lost. He was featured in MTV *Girls Night Out* with VJ Rannvijay Singh, *Haunted Weekends* with Sunny Leone, and various other shows. His work was also covered by various news channels, including Aaj Tak, Live India, News 24, Star TV, Zee News and IBN7. He also appeared on Zee TV's *Fear Files*.

Apart from being a certified commercial pilot, he was a certified lead paranormal investigator and a ParaNexus representative in India. He was also a certified UFO field investigator. He held a Bachelor's degree in metaphysical humanistic science, was an ordained minister from the Metaphysical Church of Humanistic Science, certified hypnotist and past life regression practitioner, spiritual counsellor and a life/relationship coach from the Institute of Metaphysical Humanistic Science. All this was possible because of his guru, Dr Doug Kelley, founder and president of the ParaNexus Anomalous Research Association, Inc.

Gaurav Tiwari appeared on well-known international paranormal radio shows. He earned a reputation for himself and his team internationally, and is known for his work in establishing India's first scientific paranormal research team.

FOREWORD

— ALLEN TILLER

ALIAtech, DipFamHist, 2017 South Australian
Emerging Historian of the Year, paranormal historian,
Haunting: Australia *team member*

Some people touch the lives of others in such profound and dramatic ways that they change those lives for the better. Gaurav Tiwari was one such person. Through his words, his actions, his good deeds, his research, and now, sadly, his legacy, Gaurav continues to change lives for the better.

If you are reading this book and have never heard the life story of India's greatest paranormal investigator and researcher, you are in for a life-changing discourse about spirituality, paranormal belief and self-belief. Gaurav Tiwari was many things to many people. For some, he was India's greatest paranormal expert, for others he was their team leader at the Indian Paranormal Society. He was a mentor to many, an idol to others, a sex symbol, a singer, an actor, a guru, a religious icon, a friend. But for me, he was my little brother! He was family.

I was first introduced to Gaurav through Facebook in 2009, not long after he founded the Indian Paranormal Society. He had messaged me as a cousin of his living in Brisbane, Australia, needed the help of a paranormal investigator. Gaurav was not aware at the time of the vast distances between cities in Australia. He thought Adelaide, where I lived, was not far from Brisbane, which is almost 2,000 kilometres by road, or a two-hour flight. While I could not go to Brisbane, I found his relative the help he needed locally, and at the same time, struck up a friendship with Gaurav.

Over the years that followed, Gaurav and I discussed each other's cases. We helped each other debunk or confirm footage and EVPs. In this book, you will read about several of these cases, including one in an underground car parking, where Gaurav and his team captured footage of a child's spirit. I was one of the first outside his team to see that incredible footage.

We often spoke of working together on a project. That happened in 2013 when Gaurav came to Australia and we recorded the paranormal investigation television show, *Haunting: Australia*. We met in person at the Sydney studios of Flame Productions and strengthened our bond. Over the next five weeks, we investigated eight locations across Australia. Gaurav (and the team) visited my house in Kapunda. There, my wife Karen cooked for him her chilli–plum kangaroo—a dish Gaurav had longed to taste. We put on a smorgasbord of South Australian delicacies,

Coopers Pale Ale (beer), Fritz (a type of luncheon meat), Fruchocs (an apricot chocolate) and a lot of other local produce.

It was also while in South Australia that I was able to assist Gaurav in being able to interact with Australian wildlife. For one of our show segments, we visited Cleland Wildlife Sanctuary. While here, Gaurav was truly happy; he patted kangaroos, saw Australian native marsupials and deadly snakes. The most thrilling moment for him, and the one that brought out his biggest smile, was holding a koala named Edmund.

We met in person again in 2015 when Gaurav returned for the *Haunting: Australia* tour. This time we investigated some new locations. Gaurav, Rayleen and Robb stayed with us in Kapunda for a few days, allowing us to show them the Australian way of life. When we parted ways, we returned to Facebook to keep in touch.

In the months before his death, Gaurav and I had been discussing him coming to Australia to undertake a Ted Talk-style lecture tour, presenting lectures on paranormal topics. We also discussed writing a book together and pitching a new television show. None of this was to happen due to the tragedy of his early death.

After Gaurav's death, his trusted team members at Indian Paranormal Society continued Gaurav's work. Eventually, they decided to preserve his legacy by presenting some of his most interesting cases in a book. They searched tirelessly for an author who they felt could convey Gaurav's story with the same empathy and integrity that Gaurav put into his work. They chose Abhirup Dhar from the many candidates they considered. Mr Dhar, who has had a lifelong passion for writing, also has an MBA. He has written stories across many genres, with horror, a genre closely associated with the paranormal, being the one he is most often linked with.

Society and religions dictate how we should live, work, conduct ourselves, interact and what we should believe. Within those societal rules, anything seen as 'occult', different or unusual in belief systems leads to people being accused of having mental health issues, or being given other such labels, and usually ends up in them being ostracised in some way. Gaurav had one simple mantra regarding societal regulations: *What they think is none of my business.* Gaurav truly believed this, and strove forward in every aspect of his life, not caring what people claimed about him. His reputation as someone fearless is expressed in that same mantra. Fearing the dead, the spiritual realms, is the same as fearing the opinion of the living—it makes no difference to your life unless you allow it to do so.

Gaurav had another mantra he lived by: *Knowledge cancels fear.* He believed if he could research the afterlife and talk to people about his findings, he could dispel their fears. He achieved this goal with many of his investigations and talks in India where he uncovered urban legends and long-held mythical beliefs in his own country.

In the following pages, you will read the real-life exploits of Gaurav Tiwari and his team, the Indian Paranormal Society, and his other investigation team, G.R.I.P. You will learn what got him interested in paranormal research and read of his international investigations in Australia.

You will hear from those closest to him, his team members and his best friends. And while this book touches upon his tragic death, it is really a celebration of his life and legacy as India's first modern world catalyst to open discourse about spirituality and the possibility of life after death. Let me rephrase that statement: Such was Gaurav's influence and standing that he was a catalyst to open discourse globally about spirituality, paranormal investigation and life after death. Knowledge cancels fear.

Gaurav, in death, contacted many of his team members, friends and family. You will read about those incidents in the following pages. I believe this was him, again, trying to communicate that there is more to the world than we know, and that we should not fear death, nor the afterlife.

Gaurav Tiwari was an inspiration for many, and through this book, his memory is strengthened and his legacy further solidified as one of the greatest and most influential paranormal researchers the world has seen to date.

Vale Reverend Gaurav Tiwari, my little brother. May your legacy live forever.

A NOTE BEFORE WE BEGIN

A professional investigation conducted by the Indian Paranormal Society includes the following phases:

1. Client interview/contact, wherein the client speaks to us and states what they are experiencing at their property. We also ask a few other questions and perform a short screening session to eliminate the possibilities of foul play and to determine if it really requires our intervention/professional paranormal investigation. During this phase, we also send the client a few forms, including a non-disclosure form, expectations form, permission to investigate, client assumption of risk, initial contact/interview form (client's historical data, including history of the place, activities being experienced, members who experience the activity, family members/people who stay at the place, etc.).

2. We visit the location to conduct a preliminary investigation. The moment we step in, we note down the readings displayed on our equipment (EMF/K-II meters) to see if we get any unusual readings during normal conditions (with all electrical equipment like fans, tube lights, etc. switched on and also with

everything switched off). We also use these readings as our base reading before starting the third phase, which is conducting a full-fledged paranormal investigation. Later, baseline readings are used as reference between current readings and the real-time readings that we document on the equipment.

3. We conduct a thorough investigation (we have high-end equipment like night vision cameras, motion sensors, EMF meters, infrared video cameras, DSLR cameras, etc. which we set up at the place of investigation in an attempt to document evidence or any subtle changes in the ambient environment). The goal here is not to prove anything but to observe and document any changes. During observation, if we experience anything unusual in a certain place within the property, we mark it as a 'hotspot' and try to focus on that place to see if it recurs with other researchers or if we can document anything substantial that may later provide answers for the experience of the client. This phase may (depending on the experience we have during the investigation) involve client counselling where we ensure the collective experience (client plus investigators) we have doesn't have a negative impact on the client's psychology. The goal here is to empower the client to be self-reliant and not fall prey to frauds by self-proclaimed godmen, which may impact them negatively.

4. This is when we sit down to analyse the recordings and documentations to check if we got something on our equipment. If we do manage to document

something that we feel can be significant evidence of the paranormal, we attempt to first rationalise and then debunk it, thereby ruling out any normal occurrences (sounds from stray dogs, people talking in the background, EMF spike due to mobile phones, etc.), whether the things we felt were because of something natural or a kind of contamination (that could be because of us or any technical or man-made error). If we come across a piece of documentation that passes all the tests (debunking/rationalising), we clip it and save it to share with the client. If we don't document anything unusual or significant, we inform the client about this and close the case.

5. This step is optional and completely depends on what we come across during the fourth phase/evidence analysis. We revisit the property and conduct a short preliminary styled investigation (to check if the experience we documented or experienced during the third phase can be repeated). This stage also involves us performing a cleansing session. Cleansing is performed differently in different teams. For us, we usually communicate with whatever is present in that space and see if we can help the intelligence that will enable it to stop showing its presence to the clients. We ensure this by performing a small investigation and using the experience that we had in the third phase as reference and then check if we document anything unusual.

6. We counsel the members of the family. The main purpose of this counselling session is to help them overcome their fears of the unknown and also to

strengthen their belief system. Also, in this phase we showcase and explain all the evidence that we documented.

Additional links for reference to our work:

A short guide on paranormal research – https://reflectionofyourthoughts.wordpress.com/2015/ 04/26/a-paranormal-guide-for-dummies/#more-91

A brief on consciousness/basic fundamental of paranormals research – https://reflectionofyourthoughts.wordpress. com/2016/04/ 24/consciousness-the-real-talk/

Understanding paranormal research by Rev GT (Ted Talk) – https://reflectionofyourthoughts.wordpress.com/ 2016/02/09/decoding-the-existence-of-spirits/

Current scene of paranormal research (2015 edition) – https://reflectionofyourthoughts.wordpress.com/2015/04/ 15/current-scene-of-paranormal-research-in-india-2/

Disclaimer: The above phases are not included in entirety for the purpose of narrative in the chapters.

I simply laugh at people who call themselves educated and modern by just not believing in ghosts. I believe you must be educated enough to understand the concept of the paranormal. The fashion of not believing in anything paranormal to call yourself a non-believer is obsolete in most countries in the world. Now, people in other countries want to learn and explore what was kept behind closed doors due to fear of society and losing their place in society. The world is consciously rising. I think we all should come out of our cocoon and ensure our beliefs are not based on fashion and preconceived notions. Believing in ghosts is not superstition. Superstition is believing in anything in the absence of proof. But empirical evidences suggest that we do survive our physical death. So, who is being superstitious now?

— GAURAV TIWARI

PROLOGUE

'**G**aurav ...'
A whisper in his ear woke Gaurav up in the middle of the night. He sat up on his bed and realised he was sweating profusely.

'Perhaps I had a nightmare,' he muttered to himself.

He switched on the table lamp, poured a glass of water from a jug, drank it in one gulp and then looked at the ticking clock. 3.05 a.m.

Gaurav's friends had gone out for a party and he had decided not to join them. It was a different matter that he wasn't really into loud parties, but the day had been very exhausting and he had looked forward to a good night's sleep.

The silence was like a restorative draught after the frenetic rush of the day, surrounding him like a fresh, pristine white blanket of snow on a winter's day. Tiredness swallowed him whole again. His lashes fluttered and sleep came over him again.

'Gaurav ...'

A whisper again; this time it was clearer.

Unsure if he had slept even for a few minutes, Gaurav

jolted upright. He stood up and looking around, but he could see only darkness. He remembered that he hadn't switched off the table lamp before falling asleep again.

What's happening, he asked himself, taking small steps in the pitch black room so he could reach across and switch on the lamp.

A non-believer in anything supernatural, Gaurav was still under the impression that he'd had a nightmare. But twice? Someone had called his name twice.

In the midst of many thoughts all coming to him at once, the twenty-three-year-old training to be a commercial pilot in Deland, Florida switched on the lamp. The dim light was a relief. He reached for his mobile phone to call one of his friends—not to tell him that he was scared, but to ask when they would come back. However, the battery was dead.

Strange, he thought. He was puzzled—he had charged it fully before going to sleep.

Then he heard footsteps. He strained his ears. It was very faint at first, but there was definitely someone in the drawing room. Could it be that one of his friends had come back from the party and he hadn't heard them open the front door?

The footsteps got louder. Someone was walking back and forth in the drawing room. Quite frantically, so it sounded.

'Who is it?' Gaurav called out.

There was no reply. The footsteps continued.

Gaurav walked slowly towards the door with bated breath. He couldn't understand the emotion at first. He hadn't experienced it at such a magnitude earlier. The young man was scared, for the first time in his life. His hands trembled and his eyes filled up as he reached towards the door knob. Something was behind that door and it wasn't good; he could sense it. His body felt hot and sweat started trickling down his neck even though the air conditioner was on. He gripped the knob and twisted it. With every move he made, he felt even more terrified. Meanwhile, he could hear the footsteps clearly now. The door creaked open. Gaurav's breath quickened. Suddenly, everything was silent and there was only darkness behind the door. He knew where the switchboard was, right next to the door. The lights came on; he looked around. There was no one.

I must be hearing things because I'm alone, he tried to pacify himself.

The next second, he heard the footsteps again. Someone was walking from one side of the room to the other, taking heavy and quick strides.

Pure terror surged through Gaurav's veins, icy daggers reaching straight to the heart.

'Wh-who? Who is it?' he managed to say.

The walking stopped. Silence!

'Gaurav …' It was a lady's voice; not a whisper this time.

The non-believer stood there for a while, trembling, feeling the presence of something he couldn't comprehend. As he looked into the empty room in front of him, he could sense an entity standing bang opposite him.

ONE

THE FIRST MEETING

Despite so much resistance in society about my work, I have always been able to stand strong because I followed the mantra: What they think is none of my business.

— GAURAV TIWARI

Dark grey smudges surrounded the sky above threateningly, like a predator would encircle its prey. A long low rumble rang through the cool air. Raindrops began to hit the ground and the drizzle soon turned into a torrent, pummelling everything in its way. A sense of cleanliness caressed the atmosphere, as if the water were washing away all impurities. A dense earthy smell rose from the ground, enveloping everything within its soft embrace. After a few minutes, the skies settled, as if comforted, coaxed even. The grey smudges didn't part completely, though, and the sun peeked out timidly, looking like it was preparing for an even more vicious round. And soon enough the rain bore down mercilessly on the city again, pounding on rooftops, turning the road and streets of Mumbai into a warren of muddy waters.

I peeked out from underneath the covers; I could hear the rain falling against my bedroom window. This was my favourite kind of day—when I didn't have to feel bad about not leaving the house. I got up and rubbed my eyes, remembering that I had slept very late. I'd burned the midnight oil completing my fourth book, which I would send to the publisher in a few days after a quick proofread. As a banker by day and a writer by night for the last five years, I felt it had been a very productive phase in my life.

I always felt a certain void after finishing a book, but this time it was different. I had already begun working on my next book, something I was very excited about. This time it wouldn't be fiction, the genre I'd come to be associated with. The book would be based on true incidents, terrifying ones at that.

It had all started when I contacted the Indian Paranormal Society (IPS) in Mumbai with the suggestion that I write a book based on their cases. The team members—Meghna, Siddharth, Mohan and Rith—had been very interested when I discussed my idea. Over the next few days, we had been in touch constantly, on con-calls, text messages and e-mails, till it was decided that we should meet.

Now I made myself a hot chocolate with whipped cream, sat beside the window and opened my laptop. I had been doing some research for the book at my end already. I felt confident about the project and had even discussed it with my literary agent, Suhail Mathur. When I'd called Suhail to discuss the idea, he'd been very enthusiastic, and his vote of confidence made me even more sure that I was going in the right direction.

My phone rang. It was Meghna.

'Hi, Abhirup. How are you?'

'Good, good! You say.'

'Let's all catch up today. Mohan is out of town on work, and Rith is busy too, so it will be just me and Siddharth today. Is that cool with you?'

'Definitely! Where? At your office?' I asked.

'Yes. We just got back home actually. Can we meet at four o'clock this evening?'

'Reached home? Now?' I was inquisitive since it was morning.

'We had a case.'

'Wow! Saw a ghost?'

'Yes. Let's talk more when we meet.'

Ever since I was a child, I've been very curious about anything supernatural. Unfortunately, I've never had a paranormal experience. When I was younger, I did try very hard to meet ghosts and spirits by calling them via planchette or even visiting locations I'd heard were haunted, but much to my disappointment, nothing happened. It seemed natural that, when I began writing, I would turn to the horror genre, the most intriguing but neglected genre. It was this passion that made me get in touch with the IPS—the first of its kind in the country—established by the late Reverend Gaurav Tiwari in 2009. From the little that I had read so far, and recalling Gaurav's shows on television during his heyday, I was confident it would make for a good story, a true horror one at that.

I was excited when I reached the IPS office in Malad. Walking into their office completely drenched, I folded up my umbrella and greeted them. It was the first time we were meeting, but it didn't feel like that.

'At last we meet!' I said and smiled.

We all laughed at the same time, realising it had been over a month of us talking about the project, with no actual face-to-face meeting. Our hectic lives in Mumbai was one reason.

After we'd settled down with steaming cups of coffee and tea in front of us, I leaned forward and said, 'Meghna, tell me. I've been pondering over this since the day you told me about it. How did a non-believer start believing and then go on to be the first person to begin a movement in India, at a time when there was no one to educate people about spirits and ghosts?'

'There is a chilling beginning to the story,' she said and smiled.

I took a sip of my coffee and looked out of the glass window at the downpour outside.

'Nothing better than a good ghost story on such a day, really,' I said.

Gaurav managed to walk over to the main door, still trembling with fear. Then he opened the door with a bang, rushed out and ran till he reached the elevator. He waited downstairs in the building lobby for his friends to return. They came back after an hour or so and found a very nervous Gaurav seated on a sofa. They hadn't ever seen him like that. He was always so calm, confident and positive.

'There's something in our apartment!' he told them.

'What?'

'A gh–ghost,' he stuttered, realising he had just told his friends he'd seen something he had never believed in.

'It must have been a nightmare,' one of the friends said and hugged him tightly.

'Come on, we are with you. Let's go upstairs.'

They opened the door of the apartment and walked in to see nothing there. And nothing suspicious happened over the next few days.

Then, one evening, when Gaurav and his friends were having a quiet dinner after a tiring day, a shrill noise broke through the companionable silence, becoming louder over the next few seconds to such an extent that it engulfed them, piercing through their ears, rendering any logical thought impossible.

'What the—' one of them screamed, and all the friends looked around as the noise seemed to be coming from everywhere.

It sounded like someone was scratching the windows. Someone? No. How could it be one person! The noise was coming from all the windows around them. There had to be many people, but there was nobody to be seen.

'Stop it!' another friend yelled in pain. His ears hurt, the noise was so loud and terrible.

Silence. Eerie silence.

They all looked at each other, stupefied. None of them could understand what had happened, except Gaurav, who had begun believing in the paranormal.

The very next evening, Gaurav was sitting in the drawing room with two of his friends. The others were yet to return. They were discussing books and movies when they heard footsteps. They stood up and looked around blankly, not uttering a word so that they could hear better. Yes, there it was.

'All of us can't be hearing things at the same time, right?' Gaurav asked the other two.

Just then, one of his friends gave a loud scream while pointing at the stairway that led to their individual rooms. The light was a little dim, but they could all see a pair of legs walking up the stairs. They immediately rushed upstairs to check, but there was nobody to be seen, anywhere. They were so frightened, they decided to sleep together in the drawing room that night. None of them could deny what they had experienced. But they couldn't vacate the apartment at such short notice. Also, their course would be getting over in a few weeks, and it didn't really make sense to look for another place for that short period.

'We should always stay together,' they decided between themselves. But that was practically impossible, as they all had different timings. Two days after this frightening incident, Gaurav found himself alone again in the evening. After completing some work and sending a few official mails, he wanted to get some fresh air, so he headed outside for a stroll.

There were so many questions that had been bothering

him over the last few days that Gaurav couldn't be himself, even during his classes. Though he was an introvert and didn't mingle much with people anyway, his recent behaviour was still noticeable. His roommates were troubled too, but none of them talked about their experiences to anyone else. Many wouldn't believe; others wouldn't care.

Thoughts trundled through Gaurav's brain like a train with no sign of stopping. The walk wasn't helping much and a disappointed Gaurav turned around. His gaze fell on the window of his room from where he often peeked down to see if his friends had left or were heading back. Once again fear found him; his palms became sweaty and the adrenaline coursing through his system shut down his ability to think logically. An old lady was staring back at him from his window. She didn't blink even once, or so he thought—the stare was so stern. There was not a trace of a smile on her face. She just looked at him … and kept looking. Gaurav couldn't move; it was as if he was under some kind of a spell. He wanted to scream, but couldn't. Tears rolled down his cheeks as the young man, a non-believer in anything supernatural till just a few days ago, battled the new reality he was now being forced to acknowledge.

It was the start of the weekend two days later, and one of Gaurav's flatmates had reason to smile. He had invited his girlfriend over for dinner, and had planned for her to stay over in his room. That evening, the doorbell rang and Gaurav opened the door and greeted her.

'H—' she started but then stepped back, screaming as she looked behind him. Gaurav looked back to see nobody.

The girl ran down the steps, got into her car and called her boyfriend.

'I … I saw … I saw a strange ap-apparition behind your fr-friend. You should … should get out of that goddamned place!' Then she quickly drove away.

It was at this point that Gaurav decided he wanted to delve deeper into the subject of paranormal activity so he could understand it better. He joined the ParaNexus association and began a certification course in paranormal investigation. After learning about paranormal phenomena and human conditions from Doug Kelley, co-founder of ParaNexus Anomalous Research Association and the Institute of Metaphysical Humanistic Science, Gaurav decided to grow as a paranormal investigator and dedicate a part of his life to paranormal research. He soon became a certified paranormal investigator for ParaNexus and an ordained minister from the Metaphysical Church of Humanistic Science, which meant he could conduct exorcisms. Thus began his journey to know the unknown. I kept taking notes as Meghna spoke.

'So I know a little too. I've been doing a bit of research at my end, you know. Gaurav came back to India in April 2009 and established the IPS to educate people and help them overcome their preconceived notions about spirits and ghosts. That's where this movement began, the first of its kind, and he inspired several others to follow him,' I said enthusiastically

'Bang on!' Meghna smiled.

'Now you can tell me it was the right decision to have me as your writer,' I joked and everyone laughed.

'A team called Ghost Research and Investigators of the Paranormal (GRIP) was set up too, to investigate the paranormal in India under the leadership of Gaurav Tiwari. Abhishek Garg, Akanksha Kaushik, Binoy Parikh, Praful Brar and Sameer Pandey—who contributed a lot in establishing IPS—were invited to join the board of directors. The entire idea was modern and very new to the country, but gradually it got accepted and news channels began covering our investigations too.'

'I see.' I thought for a moment, remembering shows from some years back. 'I recall watching television shows like MTV *Girls Night Out* and *Bhoot Aaya*—Gaurav was almost everywhere then. He was the face of paranormal research. In fact, I remember watching him in a movie or two as well; mostly cameos though,' I said.

'Yes, yes. That's right.'

'I'm curious, Meghna,' I continued. 'I want to know more about Gaurav Tiwari as a person, but I'm equally interested to know one more thing ...'

'And what would that be?'

'Tell me about the most spine-chilling cases the IPS has handled, will you?'

I stood up to find a socket where I could plug in my laptop charger.

'Hmm, that will take time. Give us ten minutes. I just need to make a few calls and send an important mail.'

'Yup, of course! I'll jot down a few more points I picked up from our conversation so far too.'

TWO

HAUNTED BASEMENT PARKING

The first step in research on 'spirits' is to truly recognise the 'spirit' that lives inside us.

— GAURAV TIWARI

It had stopped raining while I was listening to Meghna talk. But it turned out to be a temporary reprieve. The grey sky grumbled restlessly again and the thick clouds struggling to withstand the burden of the weight of the rain they held soon gave up. The rain poured down on the city with a roar. The sky became darker as the downpour intensified, accompanied by a fierce wind. In seconds, there was a wall of water. So heavy was the rain that the waterlogging Mumbai is infamous for had already begun, gurgling over the asphalt of the roads into already overloaded drains.

'Done with your work?' I asked after a few minutes, impatient to hear the stories.

'Yes, yes,' Meghna and Siddharth both said at the same time.

'Those experiences in his apartment in Florida must have been a truly scary experience for Gaurav,' I said. 'But it resulted in an amazing movement.'

Meghna nodded. 'We're accustomed to these unnatural occurrences now,' she said.

'Actually, before we get into the stories, tell me—how and why did you two join Gaurav and the IPS?'

'Long story …' she said.

'I'm all ears,' I said. 'Nothing like a good ghost story for a horror writer.'

She smiled and glanced out of the window. 'It was a rainy day like today too …' she began.

It had been almost a year since Meghna's father had passed away, and both she and her sister had been sensing some kind of a presence at home. Though the family passed it off as a lingering repercussion of the loss, Meghna could feel this presence even more strongly over time.

On her mother's birthday, she decided to make it more special by inviting their neighbours to a party. She baked a cake that looked like a sewing machine, because of her mother's passion for stitching. Apart from the cake, she had prepared all her mother's favourite delicacies in appreciation of the wonderful guide she had always been in their lives. Meghna's sister said she would be a little late getting back from the office, and the neighbours were asked to turn up by 6 p.m. There would be a cocktail party before dinner, and it was all planned very well. It was a day to celebrate, though Meghna still felt a void within her.

'Remember how Daddy always forgot your birthday and would wish you a few days later?' she asked her mother, her eyes filling with tears.

'Yes, he once told me he did it on purpose.' Meghna's mother giggled like a shy teenager, reminiscing about the silly ways of her boyfriend turned husband.

'He would be so happy today, Mummy.' Meghna walked up to her, sat on the floor close to her mother and lay her head against her leg.

'Don't get emotional today, baby. Go … go get dressed. It's almost time and I'm excited. Do you want me to cry today too?' Her mother wiped tears from her eyes as well as her daughter's.

A few minutes later, Meghna was standing in front of the large mirror in her bedroom. She was wearing a dress her father had gifted her on her birthday three years ago.

How I wish you were here today! You went too soon, Daddy, she thought.

She called her sister and was informed that she had just left her office, but was stuck in a traffic jam.

Just then, Meghna saw in the mirror that someone was standing in the dimly lit corridor outside the room. It was a dark figure, standing still, as if looking at Meghna. She looked closer in the mirror. Was it a trick of the light? No, it wasn't. She turned around and stared at the figure.

'Who is it?' she heard herself asking. She was nervous and unsure what she should do next.

There was a movement right then. The entity wanted to tell her something.

'Who is it?' Meghna asked again, a shiver running down her spine; and yet, there was something familiar about the entity. She felt like she knew him. Yes, it was a man—someone she knew very well.

Meghna took a few steps forward. The figure moved again. She could make out his attire then, though his face was still not discernible. The figure had on the same red and white checked shirt and blue blazer that used to be his party wear the few times he went out. It was Meghna's father. The two continued to look at each other. Meghna thought she saw him smile, and then he disappeared the next moment, leaving her with mixed feelings—she was scared yet emotional.

She rushed to her mother, hugged her and began sobbing.

'He came to wish you on your birthday, Mummy,' she said as she cried. 'For the first time he remembered the day,' she said and sat down beside her mother, who looked at her for a few seconds.

'I sense his presence all the time, Megs. He is here with us … guiding us, loving us, watching over us,' she said calmly.

I was quite speechless listening to Meghna's first paranormal experience, which—as was evident—would be etched into her heart and memory for life.

'It was after that incident that I wanted to explore these things beyond human understanding,' Meghna said.

'How did you approach Gaurav?' I asked.

'I had seen him on television and was very intrigued already. After this incident, I checked him out online and then dropped a mail, asking if I could work with him. A few days later, his personal assistant called me from his Delhi office. He connected with me over the phone after that and welcomed me to his team.'

'That's interesting,' I said.

'Siddharth joined him one year before me. I became a part of the IPS in 2015.'

'He and the team must have investigated many cases.'

'Yes. Gaurav himself was a part of around six thousand cases, both in India and abroad,' Siddharth said.

'Wow! So let's talk about the most spine-chilling ones. Which come to your mind first?'

'There are so many, really!' Siddharth said.

'Still, let's stick to the most eerie ones,' I said.

'Hmm, okay. Here goes then.'

September 2014

Gaurav received a call from Sumit Kakkar, a businessman dealing in real estate, who owned a few properties in Delhi NCR, most of which were let out for commercial purposes. It had been five years since the IPS had been established. By then, it was a name to reckon with in the field of paranormal investigation. Gaurav's training with Doug Kelley of ParaNexus, his stints as a certified leading paranormal investigator with the association as well as with the *Haunting: Australia* team had been fruitful in carving a niche for him and beginning a movement in India, the first of its kind. While he dealt with cases across the country, many of the investigations he was a part of were in Delhi NCR, as this was where he resided.

Kakkar briefed him over the phone about certain occurrences in one of his buildings. The building was let out to various banks and other corporate offices, and there had been reports of it being haunted. He said he was travelling for work, and would meet Gaurav and his team as soon as he was back. He added that he was still in two minds about consulting a professional as he hadn't ever seen anything paranormal himself. The building had a two-floor parking space, and the lower one (L1) was where certain incidents had been transpiring. A senior employee of a bank had had a frightening experience, the first to be reported to the authorities.

It was one of those days when there was a lot of pressure at work; the man had back-to-back video conferences, the final one lasting quite a long time. By the time it was over, he realised it was nine o'clock and the office was empty; so was the building. He took the elevator to L1 where he always parked his car and found no guard there. As he was about to open his car door, he heard a child laughing. It sounded like a little girl. So big was the parking space that it echoed, but it seemed like it had come from right behind him. He turned to look. There was no one there.

'Is anyone here?' he called out, more out of fear than out of curiosity. He knew he had clearly heard it; his ears were not mistaken.

Everything around was still. Dead silence lingered in the air, thick and heavy, like a blanket. A premonitory chill traced its icy way down the man's backbone and just then ...

'Uncle, want to play?'

The girl's voice came from right beside him, as if someone was standing there, near his car, someone he couldn't see but could hear. The bank employee got into the car and rushed home, too petrified to even react till the next morning when he called his senior and shared what had happened with him.

The matter was escalated to Kakkar, but he didn't take it seriously.

'It's just one rumour. Ignore!' he told the office administrator who had called to tell him about the matter.

But then, there were other inexplicable happenings. The security guards said they often heard the voices of children in L1, and a few even saw dark shadows that could not be explained. One of them who had joined work recently had been there at night when he saw four children seated in a circle, playing with each other and laughing—three girls and one boy. So shocked was he that he stood there for a few seconds, unable to move. The children looked at him, giggled and vanished into thin air. He informed the head of the security guards, who, in turn, reported it to someone in the office administration.

'Look, don't add fuel to the fire. There is enough fodder for gossip already,' he was told.

The guard, Ravikant, and another man named Bansi, who had had his own share of experiences as well, mostly at night, were found to have died by suicide a few weeks later. Whether it was linked to their experiences or not could not be determined, but another guard mentioned that the two had begun leading very secluded lives for the last few days. These deaths had raised some very pertinent questions, which had led to Kakkar contacting Gaurav. He had to show some sense of responsibility.

Gaurav and his team reached the venue one night after all the employees had left. In order to avoid chaos, the people working in the building had not been informed that such an activity would be conducted in the premises. Of course the night guards knew about it, and the office administration as well.

Gaurav had already done his homework before the visit. He had found out through his sources that the property was built on burial ground. The contractor who had purchased the land hadn't paid any heed to it and had later sold it to Kakkar without informing him about it.

The team, armed with their instruments, arrived at the building at the scheduled time, Gaurav had reached much earlier as he led by example, and punctuality was one of the skills he wanted his team members to inculcate. As with every case, they had with them thermal imaging cameras (cameras that document images in the infrared light spectrum and also detect changes in temperature), EMF meters (electromagnetic meters that measure electromagnetic radiations which ghost hunters believe apparitions emit), video recorders, motion and shadow detection equipment, electronic voice phenomenon (EVP) recorders to document sound anomalies (EVP is when human-sounding voices from an unidentified source are captured on tape, digital recording or other electronic audio transmission, and can be heard during playback).

Raj, the technical expert, had already instructed the team about what was to be done with all the equipment. He told Gaurav that all the CCTV cameras were in place too.

'Have you brought a doll?' Gaurav asked one of the team members.

'Yes,' he said. He took it out of his bag and handed it to Gaurav.

'Spirits can manifest themselves in various forms and modes. This doll will be the conduit tonight.' He placed it down on the floor, moved back a few steps and stood silent for a few minutes, observing the place.

'If you have the courage, show yourself!' he said, looking around.

There was no response.

'If you have the courage, show yourself!' Gaurav said again, this time loudly, like a challenge.

Someone laughed. He looked at his team members, who stared back at him blankly. No, it wasn't one of them.

'So you want to communicate.' Gaurav walked a few steps ahead, till he was almost in the centre of the parking space.

A gust of wind swept through the place and they all sensed some presence.

'Ah, wind in an almost closed lower basement parking of a building!' Gaurav laughed, now sure they wanted to communicate.

'Okay. We need one more indication. If you are here, play with the doll or show yourself. We are not here to harm you.' The expert repeated the same sentence twice.

Meanwhile, Raj had been monitoring every nook and

corner with a video recorder, trying to capture as much as he could. Behind him was his assistant, clicking photos with the thermal imaging camera, being guided by Raj at every step as he was still new.

Gaurav sat down near the doll. The next moment the doll moved on the floor, as if someone was there, touching it, telling Gaurav they existed and should be taken seriously.

'I see. Do you want us to leave? If so, play with it again.'

The doll moved again.

Another team member holding a video camera had been recording this out-of-the-world communication.

'Okay. Noted. But none of you will disturb the balance here anymore. You will not try and make your presence felt to anyone in this building. Am I clear?' Gaurav said sternly, his eyes doing more talking than his words.

Silence.

'Tell me!' Gaurav hollered.

No response.

'Okay, then we will not go. Raj, can you come here? I'll have to cleanse this place now and exorcise the spirits.'

There was a high-pitched sound on the EMF meter just then. Gaurav turned towards it.

'They're saying, "It's our home too",' Raj interpreted the EVP anomaly.

'Oh! No ... no ... it *was* your home,' Gaurav said calmly.

The EMF beeped again.

'"It still is!"'

'No!' Gaurav said. He then said, slowly, 'You will maintain the balance. Am I understood?'

A few seconds later the doll moved again, indicating that they had agreed.

The next day, Kakkar met Gaurav in his office to personally thank him for the investigation and cleansing.

'In our field, we tend to get careless about such matters, Mr Tiwari. Though I wasn't aware the building was built on burial ground, such things happen in real estate.'

'Careless? No, Mr Kakkar. The word is greedy,' Gaurav said, and asked him to check a video recorded by Raj the previous night.

'What is it? There is nothing here. Just the basement. I have watched the one in which the doll moves,' Kakkar said.

'Look closely now.' Gaurav smiled and played the video in slow motion, the slowest it could get.

There it was! A white apparition! A girl walked from one end of the place to where Gaurav stood, on the verge of establishing an intelligent communication with the entities.

'Yes, Mr Kakkar. Believe it or not, they exist. Quite often they want to tell us something, tell us that they also exist in this world that has mysteries surrounding us, many of which are not visible to the naked eye.'

A terrified Kakkar stood up to leave, his hands trembling while he shook hands with Gaurav to bid goodbye.

'There is nothing to worry about now, Mr Kakkar. They will not bother anyone.' Gaurav smiled. 'Whether it comes to human beings or the paranormal world, it is all about communication. Our relationship with anyone is directly proportional to the quality of communication we share. The most important part of my job is to make clients and spirits feel comfortable with me through communication. The spirits are comfortable now, Mr Kakkar. And I hope you will let them be so and be comfortable yourself,' he said.

Gaurav was right. The spirits there didn't bother anyone else again. It has been years since this case, and the premises is still being used for commercial purposes. Yes, the employees refrain from going to the L1 parking at odd hours as they must have been told this as well: maintain the balance! Empathy for both the living and the dead is important.

Siddharth visited the building two years later in 2016.

'It's peaceful and the haunting has ended,' he messaged on the team's WhatsApp group, standing exactly where his mentor Gaurav had stood two years ago, in the centre of the big lower basement parking space.

'Can we play?' a girl's voice came from behind. Siddharth's phone went dead.

She giggled.

THREE

THE MYSTERY OF LAMBI DEHAR

Have you ever thought that what you have acquired in your life is a manifestation of your intentions and thoughts? We get what we set our intentions for! A majority of paranormal cases are mere manifestations of the worries and intentions to feel, see or blame something or someone.

– GAURAV TIWARI

'Indeed, a very scientific approach to determine the presence of something paranormal,' I said after listening to the first case.

'This is how it should be, no? But still, there are people who question such beliefs.' Meghna sighed.

'But you have proof. Where is the disconnect then?'

'Sceptics may still believe if there is evidence. You can't do anything about the cynics though,' Siddharth remarked.

'Yes, true … You know, I've always been curious about his …'

'Death.' They both understood what I was going to say and said it at the same time.

'Yes. It's still a mystery for many, though Delhi Police had concluded that it was a case of death by suicide. Could you throw some light on it?'

'It's a long story, and honestly, we know only a part of it. But Siddharth can tell you more. He was there with Gaurav at the time. Right, Siddharth?' Meghna said, turning to him. I had figured by then that Siddharth was quite shy and rarely spoke.

'Hmm, yes. I was there then,' he said after a pause, a little hesitantly.

6 July 2016

It had been a few months since Siddharth had left his home in Mumbai to work under Gaurav in Delhi so he could learn from the man himself. Such was his passion to know more about the paranormal! It was a rather quiet evening in the IPS office at Dwarka, on the western fringes of Delhi, and he had been working on a few documents which would later be checked by Gaurav before he mailed them.

Siddharth was living in a rented apartment a stone's throw from the office and often stayed back late at work if there wasn't a case for which he needed to accompany Gaurav. That evening it was the same. Gaurav had gone to meet a client and had asked Siddharth to work on a few things in the office till he returned. It was about 10 p.m. when he got back.

'Sorry, Siddharth. Got a little late. Hope it wasn't a problem. My phone was dead and I couldn't call,' he said as he walked into the office.

'No, no. Not at all. What else do I have to do here? Go home, eat dinner and sleep. This is what I've come here for!

To learn from you.' Siddharth smiled and asked the office boy to bring tea.

'You are embarrassing me. I'm just a common guy like you.'

'A common guy who is uncommon for me for showing the path ahead. Much to learn from you, sir.'

'I'm glad I can be of some help to you. I see so much potential in you.'

It had been a few weeks now that Siddharth had been observing a rather quiet side to Gaurav. He was normally the kind of guy who stayed aloof from people, but when he was amidst a group, he was easily the centre of attention, mostly because of his sense of humour. He enjoyed mimicking people and was very good at it. He would mimic some of his team members by adding face swap filters available on Snapchat and would send them to the team to make them laugh. A completely different guy professionally, he led by example; he was very crisp and clear in expressing his thoughts on any topic and was loved by his followers for the stupendous work he did. He also played musical instruments, and was a ventriloquist. But all of that had been missing for the last few weeks.

Raj was the team member closest to Gaurav. Originally from a small town in Jharkhand, he was now based in Delhi NCR. He had first met Gaurav in 2012 in connection with his business of selling equipment. Gaurav needed something for his paranormal investigations and had contacted him through a reference. They had met and quickly become good friends. Raj joined as head of operations in the IPS and, over time, accumulated rich technical expertise in the field. Despite their closeness, there was a part of Gaurav nobody knew. There was a very mysterious aura about him and he tended to keep to himself a lot. That was just the way he was.

'Raj was with you today?' Siddharth asked.

'Nope, I didn't bother him. It's been a while since we met really.' Gaurav seemed absent-minded, or so Siddharth thought.

'How did it go?'

'Nothing much as of now … We might have a new case soon,' he said. He finished his cup of tea and stood up.

'Let's meet tomorrow, Sid. Go home.' He smiled, went forward and patted his back. Gaurav had a very comfortable vibe about him. Even people who met him for the first time felt they could relate to him.

Gaurav left for his home, which was in Dwarka, while Siddharth wrapped up for the day.

The next morning, Siddharth received a call from Raj. India's best known and most respected ghost hunter was no more.

A lot had probably transpired between the time Gaurav had left the office and his death, but nobody would ever know. Perhaps it wasn't just about that one night. In any case, his death was a major blow to everyone, and Siddharth was at a loss for words when Raj informed him about it. So shaken was he by the news that it took him a few minutes to recover from the pain he felt within himself. Gaurav was no ordinary man for him—he was a friend, a mentor, but above everything, a terrific human being he looked up to.

'So, what happened really?' I asked. It was not just that I needed it for the book, but I was also curious. I had always thought there was more to it than suicide.

'Arya, his wife, heard a thud in the bathroom, which was locked from inside,' Siddharth said. 'She ignored it at first, thinking something had fallen, and went to the kitchen to prepare breakfast for the family. When she and Gaurav's parents realised it had been a long time since he had gone inside the bathroom, they knocked on the door.'

There was no answer.

'"Gaurav!" His father shouted for his son, the whole family turning from worried to petrified. It had been almost an hour, and there was no sound of flowing water. They looked at each other and then tried hard to open the door. When that didn't work, Gaurav's father banged, kicked and pushed the door hard.

'Arya went to the window of the bathroom and peeped in, hoping to figure out what had happened to her husband.

'"Papa ..." she screamed in alarm—she could see Gaurav was on the floor.

'Neighbours were called and together they were able to break down the door. They rushed in and saw Gaurav sweating profusely, eyes protruding, gasping for breath. The family members rushed him to the hospital where Gaurav breathed his last, almost an hour and a half later. He died before the doctors could put him on a ventilator.'

As Siddharth explained what had happened, Meghna's eyes welled up, and the next moment tears streamed down her face. Her lips trembled until she bit them and threw back her shoulders.

I could see the grief with every expelled breath. Grief. It feels like emptiness in your heart, sheer nothingness that somehow takes over and holds your soul, threatening to kill you entirely. It gives you this heavy feeling that's like the weight of the world resting on your shoulders and there is nothing you can do about it; there is no way you can get out from under it.

It had been more than four years now since he'd left, and not a single day had passed without his team members missing him and his presence.

'What about the deep black mark on his neck?' I asked.

'Suicide. What else?'

'No, no, Siddharth. Come on, tell me. Is it not true that he had told his family members that he was being constantly watched by an entity? He was disturbed because of something, wasn't it?'

'He may have been disturbed. There might have been personal reasons for that.'

'Ahh. Like what?'

'Let's not go there.'

'I have done a bit of research too, Siddharth. It's part of my job—I want to do justice to this book.'

'We understand that, Abhirup. But let's stick to the professional part.'

'Exactly, that's what I'm doing. Isn't it true, Siddharth? Isn't it true that such black marks are signs of revenge by spirits in distress? Is it possible that the death was caused by evil forces?'

'We would not like to believe so. Can we …' I could see that both Siddharth and Meghna were a little uncomfortable and I realised I was getting a little carried away with the discussion and my intense desire to write the best version of the book possible.

'Never mind. Let's talk about this later. Cool?' I smiled and drank some water, calming down.

'So … What's the next case you want to talk about?' I asked after a brief pause.

'Lambi Dehar,' Siddharth said, probably because he knew the case better than Meghna.

'Mussoorie?' I confirmed. I had heard about the place and knew its reputation as being among the most haunted locations in the country. Every horror story buff worth their salt would know about it.

Meghna and Siddharth nodded.

1990

Close to fifty thousand mine workers are said to have died over a period of time at the Lambi Dehar mines, situated on the outskirts of Mussoorie. It is said that the lime quarries didn't have any safety regulations, and the effects of this led to serious health problems for the workers. Their deaths were painful as their lungs were affected and the workers would cough up blood. The mines, which have remained closed since the deaths, are now deserted. There is nothing there now but dilapidated houses with plants and trees growing inside them. The desolation gives it an eerie atmosphere, and if you visit it after dusk, your blood will surely run cold. An uncanny silence pervades the area, as if it has a life of its own and wants you to be a part of it.

Some people say the place is haunted by a witch who

cursed it, and though there are many locals who will laugh off these stories and tell you they are only rumours, there have been so many bizarre experiences—accidents, trucks going off the road and even a helicopter crash! There have been many reports from people of inexplicable occurrences, especially in the evening. Many have heard loud wailing sounds, not only during the evening and night, but in broad daylight too. Some have seen entities too. A local resident was passing through the mines at night a few years ago when he saw a middle-aged man standing by the side of the road, asking for a lift. He passed by, not wanting to stop, but to his utter shock and fright, a few seconds later, he saw the same man again, asking for a lift. The man was so scared that he drove on as fast as he could, chanting the Hanuman Chalisa. A few minutes later, he came across the very same person on the road. By the time he reached Mussoorie, he was so frightened that he left the hill station permanently a few weeks later.

Gaurav visited the Lambi Dehar mines several times, and on most of the trips, Raj accompanied him. The most important tour was the one in which Zee News covered the investigation in real time. This had never been attempted before by any news channel or paranormal team ever.

'Zee News or IBN Live?' I asked, recalling that I had seen a video recently on the IPS's YouTube channel.

'The IBN Live one was not with Gaurav. Raj and I went there with others. It was covered by other news channels too,' Siddharth replied.

I nodded and gestured for him to continue.

Gaurav and his team reached Mussoorie in the

afternoon. They checked into a hotel, freshened up and reached the mines in the late evening, where they were joined by the Zee News team.

'Why are we investigating it at night?' the reporter asked. 'Don't ghosts show themselves during the day?'

'It's more fun when they are more powerful. This is when it begins!' Gaurav's eyes twinkled. Raj had observed it more than once. His friend was happiest at the outset of every case. Gaurav had eyes that spoke; they were very expressive.

'Ahh, right. So, shall we roll?' The reporter asked her team members to come forward. Pleasantries were exchanged and Gaurav had a few points for the person who would be shooting. He knew a bit about camera angles and how a shooting could be more productive and impactful by using some simple tactics.

'You are an expert!' the reporter said and smiled; then they walked into Lambi Dehar.

'Raj, are we ready?' Gaurav called out for the one person who knew everything technical.

'Yes, yes!'

10.43 p.m.
Both the IPS and Zee News teams were ready and inside the administrative office. The office used to be a part of the mines; the mines themselves are not accessible to anyone. Gaurav and Raj had been there several times before and knew the place well. They had already captured evidence on their equipment earlier, but this was special as it would be a real-time investigation to be telecast on a renowned

news channel. Though IPS wouldn't be earning a single penny out of this coverage, Gaurav knew visibility was important, especially for a field that meets with so much doubt and criticism.

Raj, who had found his calling in the occult and paranormal through his association with Gaurav, loved to live life on the edge. At least when it came to investigations. Gaurav would often find him straying away from the team, visiting nooks and corners all by himself. Later, he would catch up with the team and simply smile when scolded by Gaurav. It was just his style; it still is, though he is more selective about the cases he takes up. It was often he who would catch some solid proof on camera, and Gaurav trusted his actions and judgement. But he would also worry about him. Gaurav was an emotional and caring man; he loved all his team members and wanted them to be safe while undertaking these dangerous fact-finding missions.

That night was no different. While instructing his team, Gaurav observed Raj had quietly moved somewhere with his thermal imaging camera, video recorder and EMF meter.

This guy, Gaurav thought. He knew calling him wouldn't be possible as there was no network.

Raj had a plan but wanted to keep it to himself. He wanted to surprise Gaurav with some good results. He had already placed a motion sensor light in an area he had seen the last time he was there with Gaurav, and that, he was convinced, would show paranormal activity. It was in this particular place, once perhaps a doorway, that they had heard loud noises on the EMF meter. So, a few hours earlier, as the Zee News and IPS teams had been setting up, he, along with another team member, Rajat, had placed the equipment in that area. A CCTV camera was already set up there so that any activity could be captured. Now he had left to check it and bring back his stuff so that he could view the footage himself before showing it to his friend and mentor.

As he walked towards the place, one with which he was quite familiar, Raj got a strange feeling—it was as if he had never been there earlier. It looked different. Perhaps the darkness had something to do with it, as they had mostly been to Lambi Dehar during the day. It was as if he was seeing for the first time that there was actually nothing around but a carpet of grey–green moss, years deep, and a silence that felt as old as time itself. There was nothing to frighten him but he realised that he *was* frightened … and he was honest enough to admit it. Raj felt lonesome, not so much for people, but for a sound … any sound! He turned once to look behind him, but there was nobody. Nothing! Just the same grey moss, dark sky above and dead silence.

Raj reached the doorway and felt cold, colder than he had felt in the rest of the place. He silently walked to where the CCTV camera was placed, brought it down and checked if it was working. It was. He picked up the motion sensor light as well and was about to leave when …

It was very clear. It was a man crying. Yes. A man in pain, crying for help. There was immense grief in that voice. He probably wanted to say something but couldn't.

Raj saw it as an opportunity and switched on the video recorder while the EMF meter beeped frequently, indicating the presence of an entity. Or were there several of them? Raj could hear other cries too; some came from nearby, some a little far away—he was surrounded by many tormented spirits that had not been at peace for many years.

'We are here to help you,' Raj said fearlessly.

The wailing intensified and many of the cries sounded as if they were closer now; as if the entities were moving towards Raj, wanting to communicate with him.

Meanwhile, Rajat, who knew where Raj had strayed, told Gaurav about Raj's plan.

The entire team, along with Zee News, headed to the doorway. A worried Gaurav knew he had to find Raj first.

'Was this needed, Rajat?' He frowned as they walked fast.

'He wanted to surprise you.'

'Not at the cost of a team member's life.'

When they reached the place, they saw Raj excitedly taking as many photographs as he could of various nooks and corners of the area; he had been enjoying investigating. Ghosts and the paranormal excited Raj, and he wasn't scared of knowing about the unknown.

The spirits in Lambi Dehar were in a lot of pain but probably wouldn't want to harm anyone. They just wanted to communicate. They wanted to tell people something— probably their story. The opening of the mines in the mid-1970s had met with a lot of happiness from the locals. The mines brought employment opportunities, and soon many people from in and around Mussoorie had found sustenance there. So many dreams were attached to it; with every person who worked in the mines, there was a family whose future depended on its prospects. The tragedy happened later, but the truth was that these miners weren't being treated well before it too. Many of them were practically slaves—apparently the owners had had ways of managing and blackmailing them into staying on as workers.

'This ... this place is among the spookiest I've visited so far with you,' Raj told Gaurav as he switched on the CCTV.

Raj's plan had worked! Evidence had been documented; that of a mist passing by the CCTV camera as well as an audio that sounded like someone breathing—someone who wasn't human.

Gaurav had a big smile on his face after seeing it.

'Excellent job, Raj!' He hugged him. He was probably even happier to see him alive and safe.

While the cameraman of Zee News was busy shooting everything, the reporter talked about the details. After all, it was a real-time spook fest, and the IPS team was the first ever to have professionally investigated Lambi Dehar. Gaurav and his investigative team brought attention to the mines, as they would do later to other haunted locations such as Bhangarh, Kuldhara, Khaba Fort, Kiradu Temple and Karkardooma Court.

Just then, everyone heard loud footsteps. Someone was walking in the dark passage leading to where they were standing. The reporter stopped talking and indicated for the cameraman to turn the camera and shoot what was going on there. Gaurav and Raj stood up. While the latter got his equipment ready, Gaurav stepped forward, guarding all those present as he felt responsible. He looked closely and then flashed the torchlight in the passageway.

'*Kaun* (Who)?' he asked. His voice echoed.

The footsteps stopped, but there was no answer. Each and every person felt as if they were being watched; that the team was not there alone.

'*Kaun?*' Gaurav asked again, this time louder.

Suddenly, all the EMF meters with the IPS team began beeping loudly at the same time, measuring the electromagnetic radiations that ghosts emit. And then all the camera and video recorders running on battery automatically switched off. The batteries were all suddenly drained! Paranormal researchers believe in the theory of energy and heat exchange, which suggests that ghosts have the ability to manipulate temperature and energy present in an ambient environment. Spirits need energy to manifest themselves, and batteries are a source. Gaurav's torch went off as well, and there was absolute darkness the very next second.

Then there were voices ... voices that came from around all of them ... voices that were mournful ... voices that wanted to tell them something ...

The collective whispers took on a tone of fury, got louder with every second, and then stopped all of a sudden. The spirits of Lambi Dehar had communicated that they were there.

Gaurav spoke in Hindi.

'We understand. How can we help you?' he shouted, tapping his torch on his palm in the hope that it would revive the batteries.

The Zee News team, unaccustomed to such an experience, had begun screaming.

Gaurav repeated the question, but there was no answer. Raj had figured out where the extra batteries were by now.

He handed one over to Gaurav and used some for his equipment. Their torches were working again, as well as their video cameras.

'They've left,' Gaurav said. He could feel it. 'Let's proceed to another corner.'

'We sh-should le-leave,' the reporter stammered.

'How will you get your big story then, madam? Don't worry. You are safe with us.' Gaurav smiled reassuringly as they moved.

But they stopped again, hearing footsteps from the passage. Someone was walking briskly towards them.

'Gaurav! Gaurav!' the figure shouted.

Gaurav flashed his torch towards the face. He knew the voice. Raj knew it too. It was Rajat.

But … if that was Rajat, who was the man beside him, the one who looked like Rajat and who hadn't uttered a word for a long time?

Raj looked to his right and saw the entity who had taken the form of Rajat vanish into thin air. The reporter and her team members screamed out as loud as they could and were on the verge of running away.

'It … they … they won't harm us, madam! If they wanted to, they would have already! Understand this—spirits do not want to harm living people. All they need is attention or sometimes guidance which can help them move on,' Gaurav told them.

'I … I had lost my way,' Rajat said as he joined his team.

'It's okay, mate. They wanted to tell us just one thing.'

'What?' the reporter asked.

'That they exist.' Gaurav smiled. He looked at his team, immensely satisfied with the night's work.

FOUR

†HE BACCHA HAUN†ING

I often tell my clients to take responsibility rather than blame spirits for their loss. It's human nature to blame others for something that is our own fault. But those who take responsibility for themselves emerge winners in every situation—paranormal or normal. Self-responsibility is also about NOT asking others to do things for us which we should and must do for ourselves!

— GAURAV TIWARI

Mumbai and monsoon are synonymous with each other. While people who stay indoors can enjoy watching the rain from the comfort of their homes, it's difficult for people who have to commute. This was one such late evening. Roads were already waterlogged and I thought it was wiser to stay back in the office—and to be honest, I just wanted to continue to listen to the stories.

'Let's spend the night here!' I suggested.

'Well, Meghna lives nearby. It's perfectly fine with me as I don't think I can get back home either. Not during such a downpour,' Siddharth said.

'I don't mind either, Abhirup. If the night can be utilised productively for the book, so be it. However, you will have to excuse me for an hour or so. I'll go home and attend to my family. I can bring us dinner. Sounds good?'

'Sounds great.' I smiled. 'So, what's next?'

'You know, Gaurav had attained such expertise over the years that, at times, he didn't even have to be physically present. It wasn't always practically possible as well. There were so many people contacting us. Some would require immediate consultation, which Gaurav helped with,' Meghna said.

'Any case you can think of?'

'Many. Let's talk about the baccha haunting.'

'*Baccha*? Child?'

'Let's call it that, shall we?'

'Yes!'

'This is Robin's story. Robin Mishra.'

Robin Mishra had shifted from Darbhanga to Patna close to a year ago to prepare for bank probationary exams. While better coaching classes was the main reason, he also wanted to move out of his small town. He thought Patna would be a good place to start with. It wasn't too far from Darbhanga, so he could visit his hometown every weekend.

He stayed at a paying guest accommodation on Boring Road with five other guys, Roshan, Anupam, Deepak,

Atul and Ritesh. He knew Anupam from his school days in Darbhanga. It was he who had asked Robin to move to Patna and get serious about his life after college.

Soon the various bank examinations began, and the group of friends appeared for most of them, primarily the ones for banks that had a better presence in Bihar as they didn't want to leave the state they loved so much. Sadly, when the results came out, Robin was the only one among them who had failed.

'Come on, Robin, it was the first time you appeared for the exams. We have failed too,' Anupam consoled his depressed friend. He had a point, but Robin had never been very good at studies. Robin was upset not only because he had failed, but also because he would have to return to Darbhanga and work in his father's saree shop.

'Let's plan a short trip and you will feel better,' Anupam said, trying to cheer him up.

'No. You go. I'll head home for the weekend,' Robin said, in no mood for any sort of fun. He was still trying to cope with the embarrassment from that morning, when they had tracked their results online, and he had found out that he hadn't passed—in front of everyone.

'Come on; we are going to this place near Saharsa. You will like it, and the road trip too.' Anupam would not take no for an answer. He was like an elder brother to Robin, and had helped him a lot since their school days. Robin finally agreed. It was going to take time to heal, he knew, and he decided to keep the bad news to himself for the moment and not tell his parents. Perhaps he could tell them later that the exams had been postponed? No. They knew

Anupam's parents and he would be caught lying. He had to think of something better.

The friends left Patna at 4 a.m. in Ritesh's car. It was roughly a six-hour drive, and if they reached at 10 a.m., they would have the entire day to explore the place and return at night. Anupam sat in the front seat of the Scorpio, next to Ritesh, who was driving. Roshan, Deepak and Atul sat in the backseat, and Robin sat at the back of the car.

It was windy outside, not yet dawn, and as the car raced down the state highway with its lights on full beam showing the path ahead, the friends began playing antakshari. Anupam and Deepak were the singers in the group and were making the most of it while Roshan had dozed off.

'Wake me up in thirty minutes. I'll join you guys then, for sure,' he had said, yawning and covering his face with a shawl.

'Isn't this supposed to be a group outing? Come on! Don't spoil the fun.' Deepak pinched him.

Robin tried to laugh and join in the others' fun—he didn't want to be a spoilsport—but he just couldn't bring himself to.

The road lay before them like a tarmac ribbon, albeit one that had been worn down over time. A white line ran down the centre, relatively unbroken compared to the potholed road on either side of it.

It all began when they were crossing an uneven narrow part of the state highway. Robin, lost in his own thoughts, was looking out of the front windshield of the car when he saw something. No. Not *something*. It was *someone*. A young boy wearing a very bright orange t-shirt and half pants of the same colour. He looked to be in his early teens.

The boy looked to his left, then to his right, and clearly wanted to cross the road. But what was wrong with Ritesh? Why was he not slowing down the car? If Robin could see him from where he was, sitting at the back, Ritesh and Anupam must be able to clearly spot the young boy trying to cross the road.

'Can't you—' Robin cried, fearing there would be an accident.

'All good?' Anupam asked, looking back at Robin who was in a state of shock by now. They had passed through the boy like he was thin air!

Robin turned and looked out of the window at the back and saw the boy standing there. The boy looked at him for a few seconds before he disappeared, leaving Robin trembling and very terrified.

'Look at you! What's wrong, man?' Anupam said. He asked Ritesh to stop the car.

'No! No! Don't stop!' Robin screamed.

Roshan had woken up on hearing the commotion. They all looked at Robin.

'What happened?'

'Nothing, nothing. Just a dream. Ritesh, please drive. Please …' he said. Robin was sure about what he had seen, but his friends would think he was crazy. Who would believe him if he said he had seen a ghost? They would probably wonder if he had lost his mind after failing the exams. It was better that he kept it to himself. Soon, many thoughts came to him all at once, making him drowsier than he already was. A few minutes later, he drifted into unconsciousness. And then back out. The world was a blur, and random images seemed to float aimlessly around in the pool of his thoughts, as though they were being blown about viciously by a hurricane. A tap on his shoulder brought him back to the outside world, but after a second he was lost again. He could feel somebody trying to look at him, staring at him dead in the eye, but he couldn't keep focus. The whole world felt like it was in low resolution, like a bad quality movie. Confusion blossomed in Robin's heart and he knew that sooner or later he would need to wake up; to stare reality in the face. But for the moment, he lay down his heavy head and retreated into blackness.

Suddenly he realised the boy he had seen was seated opposite him and staring at him. There was darkness all around them, but he could see him; his eyes were looking directly into Robin's. There was a wicked smiled on his face, as if he was mocking Robin.

'What do you want from me?' Robin managed to utter these words.

No answer. Just the stare and the smile.

Then the boy slapped Robin. Another one. Then another. A few more. And Robin couldn't raise his hands. He couldn't move at all. Damn it. What was wrong!

'*Abey gadhe, uth jaa* (Wake up, you donkey) …' It was Anupam who was slapping him.

That was a dream, was it? Phew, Robin thought.

His eyelids battled the sleepiness and Robin finally woke up to see they had stopped at a roadside dhaba for breakfast. It was dawn. An hour ago, the blackness was absolute, but now the mist was visible and silvery. Against this backdrop, the trees were silhouettes, still as an oil painting and darker than ravens.

'What do you want to eat?' Anupam asked.

'Nothing, yaar. Just bring me tea and biscuits when you are back,' Robin replied, searching for his book in his bag. He would read for sometime till his friends returned. Maybe he would feel better then. It had been a rough day and night.

'Okay, let's go, Ritesh,' Anupam said as he got out of the car and closed the door behind him. The others were already outside, ordering their food.

Anupam and Ritesh headed towards the toilet, which was near a forest. It was Ritesh who spotted a young boy in orange seated on the branch of a tree.

'Beta, you will fall down,' he told him.

'Come down,' Anupam added, looking up at him.

There was no expression on the boy's face—no fear, no playfulness, nothing. He simply stared at both of them and then smiled.

'Can't you hear?' Anupam shouted, and indicated for him to make his way down.

The boy started laughing at them, the kind of laughter that made their skin crawl. And then they watched him disappear into thin air in front of their eyes.

Anupam and Ritesh immediately began running. They ran with all their might, as fast as they could, till they reached the dhaba.

'To hell with it!' Anupam told Ritesh and went straight to the car where Robin was sitting with the others. They both described what they had just witnessed and Robin began shivering with fear.

'The boy … the boy …' he stammered and trembled as he remembered what he had seen: the car passing through the boy on the road, his stare, the dream.

'What do you know about him?' Anupam asked, trying to bring his friend to his senses when he himself wasn't fine.

'I … I saw him too,' Robin howled in misery.

The friends huddled together and patted each other reassuringly.

'Nothing … nothing is going to happen. Got it, guys? We are together,' they all said to each other, except Robin. Undoubtedly Robin was the most shaken by the incident.

'Let's just forget all of this and have a good time!' Anupam said.

The friends reached Saharsa, explored the town and places of interest, and realised the plan was a little too tiring. They needed some rest. A lot of it had to do with the ghost sighting, but one thing was for sure—all of them needed to sleep. So they decided to check into a hotel and leave for Patna early the next morning. It was important for them to reach the city by 10 a.m. as Robin had some work. They found a small hotel that suited their budget while serving the purpose at the same time. They had dinner at 8 p.m. and went to bed in their two separate rooms. It might have been a little before dawn when a knock on the door woke Robin up. He sat up on the bed reluctantly. Anupam and Atul were fast asleep.

Didn't they hear the knock, Robin wondered. It was a loud knock.

'Yes?' Robin asked.

Someone knocked again, this time even louder.

'Ritesh? Roshan? Deepak?' He thought it was probably one of them. Was it time for them to leave? It was dark, and he couldn't see the time.

KNOCK. KNOCK. KNOCK.

Robin walked up to the door in the dark, nearly stumbling and shivering. He couldn't figure out if it was fear, the cold or a mix of both. He was about to open the door when ...

The knock came from inside the room now! Was it from the cupboard?

Robin couldn't take it anymore. It was obviously not one of his friends. It was someone else ... and the truly scary part was that he knew who it was.

The moonlight was the only source of light in the room, and in the dim light Robin could see there was someone there. A silhouette—of a young boy, perhaps. The boy who didn't want to leave them so soon.

Then there was a loud knock on the door again.

KNOCK. KNOCK. KNOCK.

Robin screamed, 'Who is it?'

'It's us ... me ... Rite ...' Ritesh sounded frightened himself. Robin opened the door and the three of them barged in.

Anupam and Atul had woken up by now. They switched on the light.

'What ... what happened?' Anupam stood up and hugged his friends.

'I saw him again, Anupam.' Ritesh was almost sobbing, he was so scared.

'The boy?' Robin asked.

'Yes … I woke up all of a sudden and there he was … sitting on the edge of the bed … staring at us … his eyes … his eyes were evil …'

'We should leave. *Now*!' Anupam decided.

The group of tired and petrified friends quickly got ready, woke the receptionist out of his deep slumber to pay the bill and left.

'We … we need an expert who can guide us,' Deepak said as they started for Patna.

'Who the fuck can do that now, here, on this deserted highway?' Anupam asked.

'Not now, not now. See, I've already mailed him.'

'Whom?'

'Gaurav Tiwari, from the Indian Paranormal Society. I follow his shows and social media handles,' Deepak said.

A few hours later, they decided to stop at a dhaba as they were very hungry.

'Let's stick together,' they told each other, got out of the car and walked together to the dhaba.

'I was starving,' Atul said as they ate their fill of parathas.

None of them was in the mood to talk, definitely not about the ghost of the young boy haunting them. Revisiting the experience would only make them more panicky, and what they needed at that moment was some mental peace. They were at the billing counter when …

A man came running into the dhaba, screaming. He was tense and very terrified, so much so that the few people who were there all stood up and came to help him.

'What happened?' the dhaba owner, who was sitting at the billing counter, asked.

'A young boy came right in front of my truck and got crushed under the wheels. I stopped my vehicle and hurried to check on him, thinking it was a case of suicide. But there was nobody there!' The man was breathing heavily in his fear.

'Young boy? In his early teens, perhaps? Orange clothes?'

'Yes, yes!'

The friends looked at each other on hearing this. They were not the only ones who had seen the boy!

'It must be the ghost of Baccha, the boy,' the dhaba owner told the truck driver. The friends could see a shadow of fear on his face.

'This is common here on the road. There is a devi ka mandir near the highway intersection. You should go and pray there,' he said and turned away.

'Go back there?'

'Yes. She will protect you or … or the boy will follow you home!' He trembled, as if remembering something. Whatever it was must have been horrifying.

'If we may ask you, who was he?' It was Robin who asked the question.

'Oh, you have seen him too?' the dhaba owner asked.

'All of us have experienced him.'

'Hmm. We don't really know. Some say he committed suicide by coming in front of a vehicle. Some say it was a murder. Whatever it was, the spirit isn't at peace and wants its presence to be felt.'

The friends left the place, vowing never to return again.

Once they reached Patna, things got back to normal. Robin began his preparations to retake the bank probationary exams and often visited a library that was a stone's throw away from where they all stayed. His friends would all be moving out slowly, as and when they were allotted their places of posting. It would be only him left at the PG accommodation, to be joined by new faces.

But then, they started seeing the boy again. All of them felt they were being watched wherever they went. There was a presence with them always. They would turn around to look, and there would be nobody, yet they knew there was! One night Robin woke up suddenly to see the boy levitating a few inches above him and his bloodshot eyes staring down at him. Robin screamed for help. The boy simply smiled, still looking at him. None of his friends could hear him for at least a minute, and they were in the same room!

It was after this incident that they received a call from Gaurav Tiwari. Deepak had been mailing him for a few days, and when they all felt it was high time, he requested for a consultation with Gaurav over the phone, so they could talk about their experiences in more detail.

'So, what's happening?' Gaurav asked the friends.

'Sir, good evening. You are on speaker. I am Deepak. Here are my friends—'

'No time for introductions, I believe.' Gaurav wasn't rude. He was a professional and knew this was urgent. He could sense it.

Robin explained to him in detail how this peculiar haunting had begun for him.

'The spirit has latched onto you guys. He has followed you to your home,' Gaurav told them.

'What to do, sir?'

'He wants to tell you something. Listen.'

'How can we do that?'

'Try to call him. I don't advise this normally, but look, I can't be there at such short notice. I have a flight to catch in an hour or so; I'll call you back tomorrow morning.'

'We don't know how to ...'

'I'll explain a simple way to do it. I can also tell you that this ghost won't harm you. He wants to communicate,' Gaurav said. As he began giving them instructions on how to communicate with the ghost, Deepak took notes.

'So you need to start by writing all the alphabets, making sure that the characters are large enough to read. Also, write numbers from zero to nine, and symbols or buttons showing the words "yes", "no" and "goodbye". These words make communicating with the spirits easier. You can add other phrases too, if you wish. Remember to arrange the letters in one or two rows, below which you can write the numbers. Place the words in different corners of the paper.'

'This is crazy!' Anupam yelled after the call ended. 'I'm not going to be a part of it.'

'Can't you understand? There is no other way out,' Ritesh said. He felt convinced they had to do this.

Going by what the majority wanted, Deepak followed Gaurav and drew the Ouija board on brown paper. They dimmed the lights and then they all sat in a circle, with the board in the middle.

'Is … is anyone there?' Robin stuttered.

No answer. Eerie silence. The friends looked at each other.

'Anyone?' Robin was louder this time.

'We … we know you want to tell us something. We want to hear you.'

They waited for a few minutes and tried calling him again, but nothing happened.

Frustrated, Anupam stood up, crumpled up the brown paper on which the Ouija was drawn and threw it aside.

'This is bullshit,' he said, frowning.

'This is not the way, Anupam,' Robin scolded him. He turned to look at where Anupam had thrown the paper, but it wasn't there!

'It's not there!' He pointed in that direction. His friends looked there in horror. They had all seen it there a few seconds ago. Where could it have gone?

Then there was a noise at the door—not really a knock though.

'Ah, the food delivery guy must be here. He said he would be late, remember?' Atul took a giant stride and opened the door …

The lights flickered as the ghost of Baccha stood there with the Ouija in his hand. He stood still and stared, with no smile on his face, tears rolling down his cheeks. He wanted them to hear his silence.

The group of terrified friends shrieked and wanted to run but couldn't. It was as if they were all paralysed; as if they were being made to stand there by some unexplainable force and look at Baccha, to try to make out what he wanted to tell them. All of a sudden, he vanished. Robin and his friends ran downstairs to the lawn and decided they would not go back up to their rooms for the night.

They couldn't wait for morning to come. This was getting worse.

'Ga-Gaurav sir must have reached wherever ... just call ... just call him.' Anupam gave his phone to Robin.

'Sorry to disturb you, sir. But—'

'Robin, I was thinking about whatever you told me. I was going to call you anyway ...' Gaurav said as he collected his bag from the baggage carousel at Chennai airport. 'Did you guys visit the temple the dhaba owner spoke about?' he asked, walking towards the parking lot.

'No ... no ...'

'You should have. Listen, I just called a source in Patna. There are hauntings everywhere—some famous, some not so famous. That doesn't mean they are not hauntings. Visit the temple, Robin. Visit it now!' Gaurav said firmly, wanting to emphasise the urgency.

'We should ... now ...' Robin looked at his friends who were in agreement.

They all headed to the car. Fortunately, they remembered the directions the dhaba owner had given. On the way to the temple it became foggy, which was unusual as it was not yet winter. A vast blanket of white hung before them as Ritesh drove to the best of his ability. They noticed that there was no network on their phones. That wasn't normal—not at all. Maybe the ghost didn't want them to visit the temple. Maybe it wanted to stay with them. Maybe it wanted a body. Maybe it wanted to feel like a human again.

Either way, after their visit to the temple, the friends were not haunted by Baccha again.

After this incident, Robin was very keen to learn more about the paranormal. He called Gaurav.

'Sir, is it important to follow any particular religion to understand the phenomenon better?' he asked after being informed about the course that is still offered by the IPS.

'I have always influenced my students to believe in the saying, *The world is my country, and to do good is my religion.* The only thing that makes me different and more approachable from other paranormal groups in India and most of them abroad is that I have a very humanistic approach towards the paranormal. I feel the paranormal is a part of humanity and can be understood without applying faith and religious biases. I don't follow or bring in religious aspects in my work, while most paranormal groups follow faith-based paranormal concepts. I have successfully exorcised many possessed people without using religious rituals. I believe possession is just an influence of others' emotional energy on someone with a lack of self-esteem. On the other hand, exorcism is an art to make a possessed person believe again in their existence by drilling in their unconscious mind that they have all the universal power to push that spirit out of their aura and mind. I use hypnosis to assist possessed clients, while many other people still stick to religious rituals and violence to treat such cases.'

'A year later, a businessman reported similar experiences of a haunting in the same area, and Gaurav was consulted again. He never got to visit the place, but it's one of those cases that he told us about. It's documented in our records too,' Meghna said.

FIVE

ADELAIDE ARCADE WITH THE HAUNTING: AUSTRALIA TEAM

'Ghosts' or 'consciousness' of human beings that survive physical death have no relation with day or night. Paranormal activity is independent of time. But we investigate at night because the environment is silent.

– GAURAV TIWARI

An excerpt from an article in *The South Australian Advertiser*, 25 June 1887:

The enquiry into the death of Francis Cluney, beadle of the Adelaide Arcade who was killed at the Arcade on Tuesday, June 21, was continued at the Sir John Barleycorn Hotel on Friday afternoon, before Mr. Coroner Ward and a jury.

Dr. Poulton said he made an examination of the body of deceased at the engine-room, Arcade, on the evening of the accident. Found the skull fractured in many

places, and about one third of the right skull missing.
The cavity of the skull was empty, and the bones of the
face and the base of the skull were shattered. The right
arm was broken in several places, and attached to the
trunk only by the skin. The right forearm was shattered
near the wrist, and the ribs on both sides of the upper
half of the chest were broken in many places. The walls
of the chest were driven backwards towards the spine,
and the scarf skin [epidermis] was scraped off the back
of the trunk. This was probably caused by the wheel.
Death must have been instantaneous, and the injuries
would be caused by deceased coming into contact with
the machinery in the room when in motion.

Henry Harcourt, electrical engineer to the Arcade
Company, said he knew the deceased, who was a
married man with a grown up family.

When Francis Cluney was found dead in the engine room
of the arcade, it had been almost two years since the grand
shopping gallery was opened in the city of Adelaide. Cluney
had worked there as a caretaker since its inception. He was
a well-respected, trustworthy man who had served in the
army. Married with seven children, Cluney was going to
turn sixty in a few months. Though he had no knowledge
about machinery, he assisted Henry Harcourt, the electrical
engineer, in operating it at times.

On that day, Harcout had told Cluney to keep an eye
on the plant while he went to take care care of some other
work. It was assumed that Cluney slipped on the floor and
died, but many people felt there was more to it than just

that. They suspected it was not an accident, but murder. A few days earlier, Cluney had thrown two notorious boys out of the arcade and one of them was seen hanging about on the day of the caretaker's death. It is believed that they followed him to the engine room and then pushed him over to the generator, causing him to fall between the two large wheels that crushed him to death.

Since then, the ghost of Francis Cluney—nicknamed 'The Beadle'—has haunted the arcade. He has made his presence felt through poltergeist activities, has been captured on CCTV and there is an image of him as well. The site of his death is now a laundromat whose proprietor has had many run-ins with the spirit. One evening, as the owner of Manhattan Dry Cleaners was shutting down his shop, he heard someone whisper in his ear. He looked back to see no one there. A few seconds later, as he was walking towards the exit, he heard a voice more clearly. When he looked back, a dark shadow was standing there. It cast a glance at him, disappeared, and then—'Boo!' Cluney said and laughed. He is infamous for his pranks on the premises.

His is not the only spirit there, though it is he who has made the most distinguishable appearances. There is Florence Horton, a woman who was shot on Rundle Street by her estranged husband in 1904, and died in a shop in the northern end of the Adelaide Arcade. Also, three-year-old Sydney Byron Kennedy, who was gassed to death by his mother in the Adelaide Arcade, in the former living quarters above what is now the Manhattan Dry Cleaners, the same area of the shop where Francis Cluney died tragically. Sydney's mother, accused of his death, drank herself to death just six months later. Their spirits haunt the area too.

From objects moving to temperatures dropping to footsteps being heard, it has all happened many times with people there. On one occasion, an electrical contractor went to the roof to do some work and he heard footsteps behind him before it went cold all around him.

An incident happened with a family that had come to hang out in the mall on a weekend. It was a little towards late evening that they decided to leave. The father had gone to the washroom while the mother sat with her son, eating ice cream. All of a sudden, the son glared at her mother and screamed, 'You shouldn't have killed me. It was painful.'

The next moment, he was normal, as if some entity had spoken through him earlier.

In 2013, the *Haunting: Australia* team investigated this spooky heritage place that is now a luxurious retail emporium, and Gaurav joined them, taking time out from his busy schedule. Ian Lawman (psychic exorcist from the UK), Ray Jorden (paranormal investigator), Allen Tiller (paranormal researcher from Australia), Robb Demarest (internationally renowned lead investigator from the US), Rayleen Kable (medium clairvoyant) and our very own Gaurav Tiwari made a wonderful global team. He did miss his own team while at it but wanted to add this important haunted location to his body of work. The investigation would be a part of the TV show, *Haunting: Australia*, filmed over a five-week period between 1 August and 8 September 2013.

A few days earlier, Gaurav had met with an accident, but despite his leg injury, he had decided not to return to India but complete the shoot. They all travelled together to Adelaide, where they would stay at the same hotel.

It was a weekday and the arcade would close at 7 p.m. It was around 10 p.m. when the team walked in to conduct an all-night investigation. A security guard had been asked to look after them, and he handed over the key to the arcade to Allen when the team reached the venue. The owners were excited about the arcade being investigated as part of a paranormal TV show.

The team had planned their activities and everyone knew what their responsibilities were; this was something that Gaurav himself believed in doing too. Once the six of them were in, they explored a few places together and then split up. Gaurav first tried contacting entities on the ground floor, capturing as many pictures and videos as he could. Then, with his EMF meter and the camera, he limped with the help of his crutches to the balcony level of the arcade where there was a bridal shop infamous for incidents that would transpire now and then.

'Is there anyone with me who would like to show themselves?' he asked.

Silence hung in the air like the suspended moment before a falling glass shatters on the ground.

'I would like you to come forward and show yourself to me,' he said calmly after a brief pause, breaking that silence.

No response. Gaurav looked around. The silence was oppressive in its nothingness and followed wherever he moved, as if it had eyes and it watched, never blinking.

'Francis Cluney, are you here?' he asked, capturing photos while recording a video. 'I'm here to meet you.' He raised his voice a little while moving towards the space near the roof the arcade, where the ducts were. 'I'm interested in communicating with you.' He flashed his torch around in the claustrophobic space.

Right after this, his camera battery drained out. He put in a new one and resumed shooting. This too drained out in the next few seconds!

Just then, strange noises came from where Gaurav was investigating, accompanied by a quick flash of light.

'You are here, aren't you?' Gaurav asked. *My camera battery is dead. With every question, I have to change the battery*, he thought. As mentioned earlier, there is a theory that spirits need energy to manifest themselves, and batteries are a concentrated source of energy, so it's easy for them to drain energy from batteries in order to manifest.

'Francis Cluney, please say something or make some more noise to let me know you are interested in communicating with me too!' Gaurav said as he continued to capture images while facing what can be called paranormal power drainage. Usually he could take around five hundred photos with one set of batteries, but because of the drainage, he could only take around fifty. Temperature is often a factor too, but it wasn't that cold; the batteries were draining within a few seconds. Too quickly!

Gaurav then set up his EMF meter to assess the situation more scientifically, and then moved a few steps back.

'I have a device in hand. I'm keeping this for you here. I want you to come closer to it.'

Immediately, the device began beeping.

'So you are here and you want to say something. Can you bring it down to two?' he asked Francis Cluney. EMF meters have small LED lights with certain figures written near them that help the researcher to measure and document the EMF of a certain place. In order to confirm that whatever they are interacting with has some level of awareness and intelligence, an investigator will ask it to manipulate the field. This also helps to establish a decent communication pattern between the investigator and the entity. If the entity can flicker two lights or three, there's a strong possibility that what they are interacting with has some outer body intelligence.

The EMF meter flickered and beeped.

'There is a spirit here which doesn't want to show itself, but it definitely wants to communicate,' Gaurav said.

Happy with the evidence collected, Gaurav went back downstairs and met Allen, who had a wide smile on his face as well. Gaurav had rarely seen him pleased after scrutinising cases, as he was a sceptic, which did help him determine the authenticity of incidents. It was a gratifying investigation for sure.

An hour later, the six team members assembled in Allen's room at the hotel.

Gaurav showed him a photo he had captured. 'I'm worried about this,' Gaurav said as he enlarged it for everyone present there.

While near the bridal shop, Gaurav had captured the image of a little boy. He was standing in the corner of one of the shops, as if trying to hide from someone. Gaurav had rechecked the place and there were no mannequins, neither was there any reflection.

'The boy who got gassed by his mother—Sydney Kennedy Byron. He's hiding from someone, scared of someone even in the afterlife,' Gaurav concluded.

'Scared of what?' Rayleen looked closer.

'Scared of his mother, perhaps?' Gaurav suggested.

'Weren't you scared?' Rayleen asked, as she was with him for sometime, capturing those images near the bridal shop, and had felt the presence of something very depressing.

'Knowledge cancels fear,' he stated.

The investigation was a very successful one and one of the most sought-after case studies in the field of paranormal investigation.

I pondered over this line after Meghna had repeated it.

'Knowledge cancels fear,' I repeated slowly.

'From being a non-believer who was scared out of his wits after his first encounter with the paranormal to a believer who had so many experiences to his credit that he wasn't scared anymore, that's Gaurav Tiwari's story in a nutshell for you,' Meghna said.

I nodded.

'So, tell me. How much does it stand true for you? Have you felt fear after your first paranormal experience?' I asked.

'I get scared, if that's what you want to know. It's a basic emotion, after all. But I rarely feel it when I'm investigating, because if I do, I will not be able to do justice to my work,' she said.

'When did you get scared as much as you did when you saw your father's spirit?'

'There have been some instances. There was one more shocking than scary. This is what happened.'

7 July 2016

It had been a year and a half since Meghna had begun her association with the IPS. The few times she had met Gaurav had been in Mumbai, when he had come over for work. Gaurav made it a point to invite all his team members to his hotel, and spent quality time interacting with everyone, talking to them about his own learnings and experiences.

That evening, Meghna had been discussing these little-known traits of Gaurav's with her mother. She said she felt that life had come full circle because of him, especially the phase after her father's death, which had been so painful. She had felt like she was losing herself, her confidence.

'He made me meet myself, Mummy,' she said.

They had an early dinner together after which she watched a football match on television—France vs Germany. Meghna is a diehard fan of the sport. She had fun watching it, thanked God for the wonderful day and went to bed a little later than she normally did.

She must have fallen asleep, and it might have been only a few minutes later when a noise woke her up. Meghna sat up on her bed and looked around. There was no one. It was dark, and she realised there was a power cut.

She switched on the flashlight of her mobile phone and opened the window as it was hot. It had been a few hours since the long shadows of the evening had dissolved into darkness. The air outside was cool, and she could hear crickets.

'I'll go and check on Mom,' Meghna thought, because of the noise she'd heard.

She walked towards the other bedroom where her mother was. She had to cross the living room for this, and just after it and before her mother's room was a small place where Meghna would keep her computer and do her work. The flashlight shone through the pitch blackness and was the only source of light till Meghna noticed that her computer was switched on. But how could that be? She hadn't used it the entire day and, moreover, there was no electricity at that moment. How could it be on? She directed her flashlight towards the computer, went up to it and shut it down.

'Meghna ...' she heard someone say. It sounded like ... like Gaurav!

She turned around, moving her flashlight everywhere.

She couldn't breathe. It felt as if the darkness was choking her. Her heart raced and all she wanted to do was curl up into a ball and wait for someone to save her. But no one would; no one was there ... except her mother who was old and sleeping. A choked cry for help forced itself up her throat and she felt a teardrop run down her cheek.

Just then a white apparition appeared in front of her and vanished like a coin in a magic trick—there one moment, gone the next. The lights came on the next second and Meghna heaved a sigh of relief. She sat down on the floor with a thud and ruminated on what she had just seen. She looked at the clock. It was a little past eleven.

Her phone rang the next moment. She went back to her room before picking it up.

'H-hi.' It was Siddharth. It had been a few months since he had left for Delhi, leaving behind his home and a job in Mumbai to be trained under Gaurav.

Meghna was unable to speak, still dealing with the effect of the frightening incident.

'Megh ...' Siddharth stammered. 'Meghna ... Gaurav passed away today morning.'

'What!' Meghna said loudly in fear and shock.

'Yes. He was found lying in his bathroom today morning, at a little past eleven,' Siddharth said, crying.

Meghna was in no position to speak then, unable even to ask him what had happened. Siddharth understood what she was going through.

'I'll call you back,' he said and disconnected to give her time to console herself. He knew how devastating it was for all of them.

Had it been Gaurav visiting her—who had died at eleven in the morning—to bid her goodbye at eleven in the night?

Meghna had heard him, felt him too. Now she would feel his absence for the rest of her life.

The world turned into a blur, and so did all sounds. Taste. Smell. Everything was just gone. Meghna took a breath, trying to hold back the strange feelings inside her, but she couldn't. A tear ran down her cheek, and, just like that, the floodgates opened. Uncontrolled tears burst forth like water from a dam, spilling down her face. Her chin trembled as if she was a small child. She breathed heavier than she ever had before. She gasped for air that simply wasn't there. Her throat burned with a silent scream. She went to her mother and woke her up, crying ... crying like there was too much raw pain inside her to be contained.

'Gaurav is no more,' she told her mother, who was completely taken aback. She tried to console Meghna, but her soothing words made no difference at that point of time. Her daughter was beyond all reasoning, beyond all regular ways of calming.

Her mother called Siddharth to confirm the news.

'Yes, Aunty. It's true. He is no more.' Siddharth's voice was choked. He had a lump in his throat as he spoke, trying hard to fight back his own tears. He had been crying for hours himself.

SIX

PRITHVIRAJ CEMETERY AND THE LADY IN WHITE

Modern-day professional paranormal investigators use equipment to check many things. Our job is not just finding spirits. We strive to solve the human aspect of the haunting first, and then we try to attempt solving the spiritual aspect.

— GAURAV TIWARI

Ben Fernandez had been working in Delhi's Prithviraj Cemetery as its in-charge and caretaker for years. It was he who visited the IPS office and narrated his dilemma. The cemetery, located on Shahjahan Road in the Khan Market area, was something the locals lived in fear of because of a few incidents related to it that they had heard about. One of the residents of a nearby locality, quite a well-known man, was returning late from his office on a rainy night. It was he who first told everyone that he had seen a lady in a white gown and hat outside the gate of the cemetery. She had stood there looking at him as he passed her by in his car. The man had found it very strange: Why would a woman be dressed in that way, at that hour of the night? He had stopped his car immediately after this thought occurred and looked back—but there was nobody! The news spread like wildfire and a few others came out saying they had had similar experiences. Whether or not there was some truth to it, nobody could really say.

Fernandez was honest about his experiences in the cemetery. He told the IPS team that he had heard voices many times and felt a presence there.

'It's normal,' he said during the pre-investigation discussion. 'But I haven't seen any lady in white. The rumours are creating panic among the residents. I want to know if there is any truth here that I'm missing.' He pleaded with Gaurav to conduct an investigation at the earliest.

Gaurav offered him tea, smiled and said, 'Mr Fernandez, understand this before we proceed. I always approach a location for research with a non-believing view. I am not a psychic who is more intuitive with vibes. I visit a place to disprove a haunting by finding all scientific and natural conditions that could give false positives of haunting phenomena. In the process, if something happens that cannot be defined scientifically, it is paranormal for us. You need not worry. We will find the truth and nothing but that.'

9 October 2012, 8 p.m.
Gaurav and his team reached the cemetery with Artika Mehra, a journalist working with a leading newspaper. Raj had only recently joined IPS at this point, and was still

learning the ropes. He wasn't yet the expert he became later on; he was more of an intern gathering all the knowledge that he could. One thing was for sure even then though— he was a genius when it came to equipment and technical things. Gaurav trusted his judgement from the first day itself and knew he would be an important part of both the team and his life.

The previous two nights, the paranormal investigators had gone to the same area to see if they could spot any apparition, but they hadn't come across anyone or anything. Many photos were taken; videos too. Zilch.

'It could be the rain and some source of light that refracted through the raindrops and appeared as an apparition. People might have just gone overboard and seen a lady in white. Everyone likes a juicy story,' Raj told Gaurav. He was quite sure there was nothing there.

'We will conclude only when the investigation is over, my friend,' Gaurav said. He smiled, gently reminding the team about one of the key objectives of the organisation— perfect investigation with the most scientific approach to determine the truth, backed by proof.

9.30 p.m.
Gaurav decided they should explore the various parts of the cemetery in groups of two. There were six of them. He and Raj made their way to the south side where there were several old British graves.

'Let's do an EVP session,' Gaurav instructed Raj, who already knew what he needed to do.

'Anyone here?' Gaurav asked. 'We are here to help you.'

They both looked around. Nothing. Nothing at all. Just them in the middle of a creepy place and overpowering quietness.

The boughs of the trees in the cemetery twisted like contorted bones, writhing in a silent scream. Beneath them lay cold stones, each a dwelling place in which no one was home. A strong wind blew and howled, making an eerie noise, uneasy to the ears. It grew stronger over the next few seconds.

'Is this a sign?' Gaurav hollered and moved a few steps ahead.

'Yes …' A whisper in his left ear shook him.

'Did you … did you hear it too?' He looked at Raj.

'What?' Raj hadn't heard it.

'Check the EVP, Raj!'

But there was no anomaly in the audio.

'I can sense it, Raj. There is an entity here. Maybe more. But it's this one that wants to make its presence felt. Quickly, what do we know about the history of this place?' he asked.

'It dates back to the British era. That's what Mr Fernandez told us.'

'There has to be a story behind this place. Rather, look at us with all these graves around us. We are in the midst of so many stories, Raj. Stories of love, rage, hatred, betrayal, enmity, dreams … some unfulfilled ones.'

Just then there was a sudden rise in the EMF meter. The normal 0.2–0.9 mG reading increased to 7 mG and then came back to normal.

'Is your mobile phone switched on by any chance?' Gaurav asked Raj.

High EMF readings can also be caused by electronic items and it's always recommended that they are switched off when interacting with spirits in a scientific way.

'No. Rules are rules, boss. We switch off our phones much before we even reach the venue,' Raj assured him.

Gaurav looked at the K-II meter and the digital EMF meter again, trying to gauge the magnitude of the presence which certainly wanted to communicate.

Raj began clicking random photos of everything around them—the graves, the trees, whatever he could lay his eyes on.

'Okay, okay. We got you. We understand you want to communicate.' Gaurav smiled, his eyes following Raj's movements.

'Now let us know if you can hear us, will you?' Gaurav continued.

There was a quick rise in the K-II lights again. The answer was yes!

'Good! Good! Now tell us, are you male or female?'

Raj went on clicking as many photos as he could.

'One beep if you are male, two if female. Please!' Gaurav always made it a point to keep his conversations with spirits lively.

Two beeps on the K-II meter! The lady in white?

Gaurav continued to communicate with the spirit; he found out a few more details about her, and also that she was happy they were communicating with her.

'Can you show yourself?' Gaurav asked. He had decided to take a chance as it was a two-way communication that was happening. He felt positive.

'Okay, so we are clicking a pic now. Please oblige.'

Click! And there she was! The lady in white had shown herself, albeit as an apparition—in the form of a strange white anomaly in the photo.

Raj took several other pictures just to be sure it wasn't a smudge or lens flare; it was certainly not mist or fog as the weather was clear, and it wasn't smoke either. It was genuine.

Gaurav and Raj moved to other areas to investigate, but the initial readings werethe best they obtained. It was 11.11 p.m.

Artika, the journalist, was with Anshul, a psychic who was working with Gaurav's team temporarily. In the quest for truth and nothing but the truth, Gaurav often invited others to join his investigations. He believed that the experiences they might have would make the proceedings and conclusion thereafter more authentic.

It was around 1 a.m., and they were near the same British-era graves. Artika, who was doing an article on the IPS, had been keen on accompanying Gaurav and his team not only for professional reasons but also because their job had sounded exciting to her. However, she didn't foresee that it would take a lot of time to unravel the truth and that the investigation would continue for eight hours in the cemetery. She had been feeling tired since midnight itself, and now felt like she couldn't take it anymore.

'I need to rest a little,' she told her partner, who was at the different end of the spectrum—he was getting more energetic as the hours passed.

'We should stick together,' Anshul said, giving her a stern glance.

'So you sit too, no,' she said, dusting an old dirty bench in a corner.

'I have work to do. This place isn't too happy. I can sense it.'

'Places can be happy or sad too, kya?' she asked teasingly.

'More than people. They have seen more of life and death than us. And Artika, many who have met with unnatural or terrible deaths must have been buried here. I suggest you move out of here.'

'Nothing doing. I'm with you guys in this. You go ahead and take a round there. I'll catch up with you,' Artika said.

So Anshul carried on with his work and Artika sat down on the bench. The dusting hadn't helped much, she thought. The place wasn't very well maintained. But, after all, it was a cemetery, not a shopping mall! It wasn't the caretaker's fault.

Thoughts of the night and her first experience visiting a haunted place occupied her for a minute or so when …

There was a whisper in her left ear. She stood up, frightened. It hadn't been too clear, but she knew it wasn't her imagination. Artika shouted for Anshul—he was a little far away and busy doing his work. But it seemed as if he hadn't heard her. She shouted again, screaming for him. No response. It was strange. He wasn't so far away that he wouldn't be able to hear her. Especially because she was calling for him at the top of her voice and the place was so quiet. Something was wrong. Artika could feel a presence near her. Her mind told her it was just her imagination, her heart told her that the mind could be wrong, and her body confirmed it—a shiver ran down her spine as the whisper came again. Artika ran towards Anshul—ran with all her might.

'Couldn't … couldn't you hear me?' she asked, trying hard to catch her breath.

'Couldn't you?' a lady's voice came from just behind her.

Artika turned around to see the lady in white! She was wearing a frilled white gown and a hat. She smiled and disappeared into thin air the very next second!

'Look …' she turned to say to Anshul, though she knew it was too late; the figure had disappeared. But … but where was he? There was nobody there, not a single person to be seen nearby or even at a distance.

'Where the fuck is—' she screamed and ran again. It all felt like a terrible, terrible nightmare! But it wasn't!

When Artika met the others a little later, she found out that Anshul hadn't been with her at all near the British graves.

'I … I lost you,' he told her.

'But … you were there! What nonsense! Are you playing around with me?' she yelled.

'It wasn't me,' he said again, looking at Gaurav, indicating that he should console her.

'Let's get out of here in some time and then talk,' Gaurav told the team.

It was at 4 a.m. that the team finally wrapped up and met Fernandez at the gate; the caretaker had been waiting for them for an hour or so.

'How did it go?' he asked, obviously curious.

'I'll tell you if we can have tea somewhere. Possible?' Gaurav smiled, looking at his tired team.

'I know just the right place. There is this small tea shop that opens very early in the morning. Walk?' Fernandez asked and led the way. Gaurav and his team followed just a little way behind.

'Mr Fernandez, is there anyone called Marie who was buried in the cemetery?' Gaurav asked as they sat on a wooden bench and ordered adrak waali chai for everyone.

Fernandez looked at him blankly for a few seconds. Gaurav understood that he had got it right.

'We had asked her name before taking the picture. And guess what, guys? Listen to this.'

He played the EVP recorder.

'Marie …' A female voice, and quite clear at that.

'The first person to be buried in the cemetery was one Marie Smith. She died in the early 1940s, I believe. There are six other graves belonging to women named Marie as well,' Fernandez told them after a brief pause, before congratulating the team for yet another successful investigation.

'You see, Mr Fernandez, sometimes they want their presence to be felt. From what I can make out, she's not going to do any harm outside the boundaries of the cemetery. But you take care and stay away from the British graves at night. It's unhappy. Her death was an unfortunate one and she is stuck there. See, if a spirit believes it can't move out of a place, it gets stuck,' Gaurav said. He told Fernandez that he would send him an official mail when he reached the office in some time.

'Go home first, sir. Get some sleep. This can wait,' Fernandez told him.

'Won't be able to sleep until the work is completely over!' Gaurav said and bid the rest of the team goodbye.

'Guys, please excuse me for an hour or so. Abhirup, Siddharth will continue till I return. Sounds good?' Meghna asked.

I glanced at my watch. It was 10.45 p.m.

'Late dinner?' I asked.

'You must be hungry,' Siddharth said.

'Not really, or I'd have cribbed! I speak my mind, you see.'

'Come on, we need to sit through the entire night here.'

'Yes. Exciting, no? Bring something light then, please?'

'Sure, sure.' Meghna smiled, put on her bright yellow raincoat, opened her umbrella and rushed out in the heavy rain.

'Don't worry. She lives nearby.'

I nodded. 'Sid, tell me, I'm curious—'

'You are, you are! We know by now.'

That was the first time I'd seen Siddharth laugh that evening. Shy guys opening up in a conversation confirm it's going in the right direction!

'Didn't you call Gaurav's spirit after his death? I ask this knowing your attachment to him and your expertise in the field.'

He beamed.

2 September 2016, Gaurav Tiwari's birth anniversary

It had been close to two months since Gaurav had passed away. Death wasn't kind. It snatched where it could, taking a man away when he was way too young. It didn't pretend to care; it didn't pretend to distinguish. Perhaps the hooded veil of death had hung over Gaurav for a long time, always threatening. But it had never touched Siddharth quite so closely. He returned to Mumbai a few days after his mentor's supposed suicide, devastated at what had happened. It took him more than a month to recover even a little. He would sit staring blankly at nothing for hours, his eyes sunken and haunted, his mind cold and empty. His case was similar to Meghna's, who had cut off from the world for some time after hearing the news from Siddharth. But it was also Meghna who had got the team in touch with each other again. She was the more mature one and had dealt with the loss of a loved one earlier, when her father had passed away; hence she was perhaps a little more accustomed to the biggest truth of life.

'Death is only the end of a chapter, my friend,' she remembered Gaurav telling her and the team during her first field visit with them. 'Don't mourn the passing of a life well lived; celebrate it,' Gaurav had told a lady who had recently lost her husband and was having strange visions at night. 'Count the times your souls smiled together, when they reached out invisibly yet tangibly and touched. As this body makes ready to return to the soil, his spirit will watch over you and live in your heart. It will bring sadness as it transforms to this new way of connecting, yet this is a part of living.' He told her not to forget the grief for which she had needed the consultation with him.

After an afternoon of reminiscing, Meghna had called Siddharth.

'It's the second of September tomorrow, Siddharth.'

'Yes, I know. Makes me sadder,' he said.

'I want to meet him. Let's.'

'You mean …'

'Yes, you know.'

They were in the outskirts of Mumbai, a few kilometres from Panvel, and standing before a derelict house. It wasn't normal weather for the time of year. An immense storm could be heard in the distance, echoing through the silent night. Lightning ripped the inky sky. The silver hues in the clouds became like molten silver, swirling, ripples radiating. They walked up to the door of the house; it looked like it needed a coat of paint. Meghna pushed the handle of the door down after putting in the key and it creaked open, the sound becoming whispers that filled the room. They entered the house where Gaurav had once conducted an investigation with them and said jokingly, 'I love this place. If you want to find me after my death, this is where you should try to call me.'

The entrance hall was airy and eerie. A breeze blew down the corridor and grasped Siddharth with its chilly touch. The furthest door from them had been left ajar, allowing a glorious amber glow to meander like a narrow stream across the hall. Siddharth's mind told him not to move, but his body dragged him there, as if he were under some sort of hypnotic spell.

'Siddharth, don't!' Meghna whispered.

'It's him,' he said.

'You never know if it's really him or another entity luring us in.'

Meghna held Siddharth's hand and asked him to concentrate on calling Gaurav's spirit. They had chosen to do it in the house because of Gaurav's fondness for it. The owner who lived in Mumbai, near Meghna's residence, had been kind enough to hand them the keys. After all, Gaurav and his team had helped him and his family when it was most needed.

This wouldn't be a professional investigation— both Meghna and Siddharth were very clear about this. Neither would their experience be documented. They just wanted to meet Gaurav from the afterlife, especially because the day was very significant. However, they had carried their equipment. Siddharth, who is an expert on sound anomalies, had switched on the voice recorder much earlier so that he could later analyse it. Meghna, a specialist in taking photos, had her camera with her along with an EMF meter.

'Gaurav, we would like to know if you are here with us,' they both said at the same time.

The breeze felt a little more chilly; or was it just their imagination?

'Are you here?' Meghna asked. She looked around and started taking photos.

'We miss you, sir. We miss you a lot. Why ... why did you ...' Siddharth wanted to know a lot of things but was getting emotional. 'Why did you end your life?' he managed to complete the sentence.

The EMF meter beeped! They were in the midst of some activity!

Then there was a very bright light, the kind of brightness that causes the eyes to close involuntarily, and warms the skin. It came from outside the front door.

'Could it be someone trying to find out if there are people inside? The person must have heard us ...' Siddharth mumbled as he walked up to the window. He looked out, but he couldn't see anyone.

'It's him, Siddharth! He always had a penchant for grand entries!' Meghna said. 'You are here?' Meghna said as she smiled. Tears rolled down her cheeks as well as Siddharth's. Tears of joy!

SEVEN

A STRANGE CASE IN MUMBAI

*When people talk about ghosts and the paranormal, in
90 per cent of the cases, there is a scientific explanation
behind it. Maybe it is due to a natural occurrence or
has some logical explanation. We consider only those
phenomena as paranormal or beyond normal which can't
be replicated in a science lab.*

— GAURAV TIWARI

December 2015

It had been six years since Gaurav had established the IPS.
Given the nature of the field, the ride had certainly been
a rollercoaster one, and one in which it had taken time to
gain acceptance. What helped, apart from dedicated team
members sharing the same passion, was the coverage
Gaurav managed to get in the media. He was featured in
many national and international TV and radio shows. There
was MTV's *Girls Night Out*, in which Gaurav featured as
both a mentor and a judge with Rannvijay Singh. It brought

the craze of paranormal investigation to India. There were other shows, and then, of course, he featured in more than sixty news channel shows, promoting paranormal research in India.

However, this didn't mean that he and his team made a lot of money. Contrary to what people thought, they were running at huge losses. The money earned from investigating cases didn't cover the cost of running operations. This included an office in Dwarka that they had taken on rent.

Thanks to the media exposure, though, IPS had become a brand to reckon with by 2015. Needless to say, the team was busy and Gaurav was a tad busier, both on the professional and personal front. He tried hard to strike a balance between his demanding, unusual profession and his family, who were not quite happy with what he was doing with his life. His marriage had also been fixed by this time, and Gaurav was to get married on 28 January the next year. More on that later. But this was that phase when it wasn't possible for Gaurav to be physically present for all investigations. He wasn't worried really, not about this. Over the years, he had built a very dynamic team who had stuck by him, and he himself was very protective about all of them. The incident described below happened during this period. Meghna and Siddharth were joined by Rith and Mohan in this investigation.

Meghna was the level-headed one in the team, and Siddharth the shy and quiet one. Rith is a radio jockey by profession now, but back then, he had recently relocated to Mumbai and was studying in college, a cool dude with a sense of humour. Mohan, on the other hand, is the thinker in the group. Not really shy like Siddharth, but quiet like him for sure. He is known for his unique ways of gathering evidence. He works in the navy now, and is available for cases only for six months a year.

One day, Meghna received a call from an ex-colleague who requested the IPS team to visit her aunt's place in South Mumbai. She rang up the lady concerned and was told about a few incidents that had been transpiring in the old apartment over the last few years.

'It's better we visit you and talk,' Meghna said and connected with Siddharth, Rith and Mohan after she hung up.

'Let's call Gaurav. He can fly down in the evening,' Siddharth told them on the con-call.

'Sid, we know he is very busy these days. Just drop him a message and a mail both. We can do this together, can't we?' Meghna said, and prepared to wrap up at her day job. It was 5.30 p.m., and she could ask her reporting authority for permission to leave a little early.

It was only around 8 p.m. that they all could reach the place from various parts of Mumbai.

It wasn't one of those posh South Mumbai apartment buildings. Decades ago, before the concept of flats had become normal in other parts of the country, Mumbai was already a little ahead in terms of modernisation. The standalone building was probably built then. Next to the fancy architecture of the new, this one almost looked like it had been beamed in from an old-fashioned horror movie; nothing good ever comes from buildings beaten down by endless seasons of weathering. Three of the five floors of the building were unoccupied, and to the local kids, it was more alluring than the corner store where they got their candy from. A few would break in with flashlights, eager to find a souvenir to show back at school. There had been a few cases of teens falling through rotten stairways, but mostly they only hung around long enough to break another window downstairs or lift an old photograph from a wall, or else a peeling of yellowed, blistered wallpaper.

The family lived on the topmost floor. Meghna had to ring the doorbell thrice before someone answered it. It was her colleague's aunt, an elderly lady in her early sixties.

'Good evening, Meghna,' Mrs Pawar greeted them with a smile and let them in. 'Tea?' she asked as they sat on the comfortable sofa in the drawing room. The building might be old and in poor shape, but the family had maintained their apartment well. Meghna knew that Mrs Pawar's husband had passed away a few years ago. The family had been into business before, and when it had failed, the son, Ankit, had taken up a salaried job. He now worked with a corporate whose office was in Bandra Kurla Complex, and was expected home soon.

'So, should we wait for him?' Meghna asked Mrs Pawar.

'Let me tell you what's been happening here in the meantime.'

'We are all ears!'

Over the last few years, she said, strange incidents had occurred in the apartment; they didn't occur often, but the paranormal activities had been on the rise in the last few weeks, after there had been a discussion on selling the property and relocating.

One night, Ankit was sitting on the sofa, watching a movie. His mother, wife and son were fast asleep. It must have been around 2 a.m. and he had had a few drinks. Earlier in the evening he had been working on his laptop which he had kept on the dining table, close to where he sat. All of a sudden, he realised that it was not there. Now, he knew he might be a little tipsy, but he was still in his senses, and he remembered clearly that he had kept it on the table. He got up and searched for it but could not find it. Though he was sure it wouldn't be in his bedroom, he went there and looked for it there too. When he came back, there it was! The laptop was back on the dining table.

'Apportion and asportion,' Rith remarked.

'What's that?' Mrs Pawar asked.

'In our parlance, apportion means objects disappearing and asportion means objects reappearing. It's quite a common phenomenon.'

Ankit discussed the incident with his family the very next morning, but his wife blamed it on alcohol.

'Maybe...' he said—he wasn't in a state to defend his experience.

Over the next few days, though, he had the same experience with his car keys. Every morning, he failed to find it where he always kept it in the evening when he returned home. One day, he searched for it in the entire house after texting his reporting authority that he would be late, only to find it later inside the car.

'It's impossible. I clearly remember I brought it upstairs with me last evening.' He was thoroughly baffled.

The goings-on had begun affecting him personally and professionally. But what happened one night left him petrified. He had woken up with a jolt a few minutes before dawn and realised he was thirsty, so he walked to the fridge near the drawing room with half-closed eyes. There was a large framed photo of his father hanging in the drawing room. Ankit opened the fridge, took out a bottle of water and drank. It was so silent that he could only hear the sound of himself gulping water. Then he heard another sound, and it was coming from the drawing room. As if someone was slowly banging on a wall. It couldn't be his wife or son, as he knew they were sleeping. Could it be his mother? Ankit went to the drawing room and switched on the light, and to his horror, at that exact second, the framed photo of his father fell down, the glass shattering to pieces.

'That's object manipulation,' Rith said. The doorbell rang then.

'It must be Ankit,' the lady said and went to open the door for him. He walked in, tired and scared—tired because of the hectic day at work, scared because he had had to come back home.

After greeting each other, Ankit joined them in the discussion.

'Your wife and son aren't around?' Meghna asked.

'I didn't want to risk their lives. We sent them away to my in-laws' place in Nagpur for a few days.'

'I see. When?'

'Today morning, after yesterday's incident,' Ankit said.

The previous evening, the family had asked a real estate agent to visit them. It had been a few weeks since Ankit had decided they should sell the property and purchase one in the suburbs. The cost of living would be low there, and they would have a handsome sum of money even after buying a new flat. He had researched everything after discussing it with his family. The paranormal activities had increased after Ankit had made the decision, but it was only he who had had these experiences so far. The previous evening, though, the entity had made it clear to everyone present in the house that it wasn't happy with the decision. Not one bit.

'We are okay with it, Ankit,' his mother had said after he told them he had found a good apartment for them in a posh society in Navi Mumbai.

The next second, they heard the light switch go off and it was pitch dark. His wife walked up to the switchboard, flashing her mobile torchlight, to find that it was indeed turned off. She turned it back on and joined them.

'Could be a glitch,' she said.

But the next moment, they all heard it being switched off again! Someone then switched it back on. The family was frightened and gathered close to each other.

Off! On! Off! On! Off! On! Off!

Then they heard it.

A voice, not very clear, but a voice for sure. It wanted to tell them something.

The family spent the night at a nearby hotel and, in the morning, Ankit made sure his wife and son left for Nagpur.

This case had a strange effect on Meghna herself, which she has still been unable to explain. As the team had approached the residence, she had suddenly developed a terrible headache and felt an eerie uneasiness. It was only the beginning.

'Could you show us the hotspots?' Meghna asked them.

'As in? We're not accustomed to your jargon, you see.'

'Places where most of the activities occurred,' she explained as the team unpacked their equipment.

They started off with EMF readings in the place, which were quite normal; there were no fluctuations.

'Mr Pawar, it's you with whom the entity has been communicating in its own ways so far. Yesterday's incident was an exception. We suggest you help us in this EMF session. I'll tell you how,' Mohan said.

The team got two EMF meters placed just to be sure that what might happen in the next few minutes would be caused by a paranormal presence in the house and not because of electronic devices. Ankit was told to start interacting with the entity as the IPS team observed.

Gathering his courage, Ankit said, 'Whoever is here, I want to talk to you.' It did help that he knew the country's best and first organised paranormal team was with him.

No response.

He tried again.

The EMF meters started documenting spikes in the EM field a few minutes later. Ankit trembled with fear and took a step back. His mother was asked to spend the night at a neighbour's place as she was an elderly lady and what she might see could seriously affect her health.

'If there … there is a gh-ghost here, show us by manipulating only the left EMF meter,' Ankit said, as guided by Meghna.

Instantly, only the left EMF meter showed a spike. Now sure that there was a supernatural presence in the house, Meghna started taking photographs. Rith and Mohan moved together to the kitchen, while Meghna and Siddharth went to the bedroom to investigate there.

'I feel we need to—'

Siddharth couldn't complete his sentence as the door slammed shut behind them! They tried to open it but couldn't.

The lights began flickering and the space was filled with darkness. The darkness grew till it surrounded the two, as if it were the end of the world for them. But both of them knew this was when the entity might communicate better. The EMF meter kept spiking and Siddharth switched on the EVP as well, so he could analyse voice anomalies later.

'Is there something you want to tell us?' he asked.

The darkness grew denser till they could not even see the lights flickering. A pungent smell hit their nostrils, like that of rotten eggs.

'Tell us!' Meghna screamed, and it was partly due to fear for sure.

She held up her camera to take photographs, but a force hit her hand hard and it fell.

The next moment, it was all gone—the darkness, the smell. Siddharth tried the door again and found he could open it now. The two rushed out of the room, joined Rith and Mohan and told them about what had happened.

'Play the EVP recorder,' Rith said, pointing at the EVP in Siddharth's hand.

The voice was clear. The entity had spoken to them. It said, 'Don't sell the house.'

It was a Class A EVP and very rare to receive such clarity of voice during investigations.

'There it is,' Rith said. 'There's the reason for this haunting. I felt it too; heard it. I was going to the kitchen to drink some water when I felt a strong presence surrounding me. Then there were heavy footsteps, as if it wanted me to hear it.'

'Mr Pawar, can you please let us know about this property? When did your family occupy it? Who lived here before you?' Meghna asked. Ankit had been following them wherever they went, but had chosen to stay a few steps behind.

'We are the first owners, Meghna.' He understood where the discussion was going, but he had to be honest with them.

It turned out that their ancestral house had stood on this plot of land. His father had had to sell it to builders many years ago when he was in dire need of money. An apartment building was constructed, and the family got one floor. Ankit's father had been very emotional about the place. It was where he was born, grew up and lived all his life; selling the house was an emotional trauma he had to go through, but there wasn't any option really, such was the financial condition of the family at the time. But he would never want to move from there; neither would he want his wife and son to do so.

'This is home,' he had said a few days before his unfortunate death. 'Don't go anywhere. I'll be here too, with you,' he had said to his wife once during his last days.

It was most certainly Ankit's father who hadn't left the world and wanted to remain attached to his 'home' in the form of a spirit. He watched over his family there, and would sometimes try to make his presence felt. But when his son decided to sell the property and move to the suburbs with the family, the spirit was irked and became more active, trying to communicate his disapproval to them.

The IPS team left the place in the early morning, reached their respective homes and caught up with some well-deserved sleep. Siddharth woke up in the late evening and started the post-investigation work in his room. He was analysing the voice anomalies and had his headphones on when there was a loud knock on the door. It was his mother.

'Who is here?' she asked when Siddharth opened the door.

'Just me, Mom. Why?'

'No, no. I heard a lady's voice very clearly. It came from here.'

'No way. You must have misheard, Mom,' Siddharth said and she left the room.

A few minutes later, Siddharth thought he heard a faint giggle. He stood up to look around, but there was nobody there. He sat down on his chair again, and then he heard footsteps in the room. This time, it was clear, and he was sure about what he'd heard. The next second, his wardrobe door opened on its own. He had understood by then that there was a presence in his room; perhaps it had followed him there. He confirmed it by doing an EVP session.

'Anyone here with me?' he asked.

The anomaly sounded like it was saying, 'Yes.'

The lights went off and he felt a breeze encircling him, although all the doors and windows were closed. It was something evil; Siddharth could sense it. Then the air felt denser followed by an eerie silence—the kind that lingered and made him uncomfortable.

Siddharth's phone rang just then. It was Meghna.

'Sid, Sid!' she shrieked. She had found something bad, really bad.

'There could be … could be more spirits there … I analysed all the photos. I noticed this in ones where you are present and I had to tell you now …'

'Noticed what?'

'The manifestation of a goat's face with huge horns …'

'The devil …' Siddharth trembled.

Meghna was deeply affected after this investigation; she felt that an energy had latched onto her as well. Her demeanour completely changed for a few days and everyone around noticed it. She called Gaurav to consult about the negative thoughts she had been having due to it, and was surprised to hear from him that her voice sounded very different over the phone. He recommended that she cleanse herself and so she did. The process took a week.

The team revisited the place a few days later as requested for a cleansing. Again Meghna felt uncomfortable just before reaching; she experienced headaches and palpitations. She messaged Gaurav about this, and he advised her to leave the place if she wasn't feeling well.

But she wanted to continue with the investigation and face whatever had followed her home, find answers to all the unanswered questions she had been pondering over.

'I'm extremely proud of you,' Gaurav texted. Meghna smiled reading it. A word of appreciation from her mentor meant a lot to her and the team.

Ankit had earlier informed Siddharth that he had called priests and other religious practitioners home, and they had used sage to cleanse the house. It's called smudging—a way to energetically cleanse a place by using sage to bring in positive energy. The IPS does not resort to such practices unless requested. Ankit said that the other technique used was with a Buddhist singing bowl. This bowl vibrates and produces a rich, deep tone when played, and it is believed to have the same effect as sage.

'If I were a spirit, I would ask, is the world different for you when it is dark everywhere? Or when you can't see anything around? Think for a moment that you've lost your sight. Where do you live now? What is the world for you now? Will you live mentally, or by your intuitions to understand this life?' Gaurav had said this to Meghna during her first few days with the IPS, and it had stayed with her.

'Gaurav, this was the first case that we undertook without your physical presence. Just wanted to tell you that we handled the situation just like you ask us to—with empathy for spirits,' Meghna told Gaurav after the case was solved.

'I know, Meghna. Even if you hadn't told me that, I'd still know. I told you, I'm extremely proud,' Gaurav messaged with a smiley. He felt content that he had been able to set up a dynamic team so passionate about the work that he could trust them blindly.

'See, Candy! Dreams do come true.' He kissed the wet little nose of Candy, his furry baby, a Pomeranian.

Candy licked his face in reply.

Anyone who knew Gaurav knew about his immense love for animals, especially exotic animals. He had in his house many animals, including an iguana, a corn field snake, a python, tarantulas, scorpions, falcons, rabbits, multiple species of aquatic animals like a manta ray, flowerhorn, eels, sharks, snapping turtles, frogs, etc. He also loved birds, particularly cockatiels and ducklings. He had a fear of lizards, but bringing into his house an iguana changed that for him. As he put it, knowledge cancels fear!

He once told Siddharth, 'I would love to have my own exotic pet farm in Australia post my retirement from this field. Come and visit me whenever you want to!'

EIGH†

KARKARDOOMA COUR†

*The strongest tool that can treat a person's brush with the
paranormal is a strong belief system. The way we see the
world is exactly the way we think about it.*

— GAURAV TIWARI

Bhavesh Tyagi, an old security guard nearing his
retirement, had been working in the Karkardooma
Court in east New Delhi for twenty-one years. A rebellious
young man back in the day, he had left his village in Uttar
Pradesh and settled in the capital city with a woman he
was in love with. She was from a different community, so
they'd had to elope. After a few odd jobs here and there, he
got an opportunity to serve the Karkardooma Court when
it was established in 1993. Often he was required to do
night shifts as well. He strongly believed and pointed out
to many people working there that the place was haunted.
But it was only in 2014 when a video went viral that the
paranormal activity in the court came to light. In the video

footage of the office and library, taken in the wee hours of the morning, a white figure can be seen emerging from a wall, computers are switched on of their own accord, drawers open and files fly out. In fact, the incidents in the video occurred after a string of events known only to a select few. One night, Tyagi was doing the rounds and was in the hallway when he observed the light in one of the rooms to his left was still switched on. He assumed that the last employee to leave had forgotten to switch it off, and so Tyagi walked to the room.

Through the glass door, he could see someone sitting on one of the chairs, still and silent. Tyagi looked at his watch. It was 11 p.m.; he hadn't known an employee was working so late. How could it be possible?

He pushed opened the door to ask the man what he was doing there so late, but then froze—there was nobody there! The man had disappeared in the blink of an eye!

The news spread quickly among the employees over the next few days, and soon it was a hot topic for discussion. Raman Sharma, joint secretary of the Shahdara Bar Association, had had his own experience, which he then shared. For years he had been saying that the courthouse was haunted and there was definitely some supernatural activity in the place. Once he and a colleague were returning to their chambers late in the evening when they heard loud knocking and saw a padlock swinging wildly back and forth, seemingly on its own. After that horrifying experience, he had always made sure to leave the premises before nightfall.

It turned out that Sharma and Tyagi were not the only ones in the court who had stories to share. Other employees began talking about things they had been observing that were inexplicable in nature. For instance, computers that were shut down in the evening before employees left would be seen switched on the next morning when they returned.

The library is in one of the several concrete buildings which have open-air corridors that, during the day, are filled with witnesses, suspects and lawyers. To say the place is dusty would be an understatement. The librarian there, a middle-aged man who lived nearby, had some pending work and stayed back a little late one evening. At around 8 p.m., he heard a few voices coming from the extreme corner on the left of the library. He thought they might be employees in the midst of some discussion.

'Shhh!' he said, reminding them that it was a library and they needed to be quiet.

'Shhh!' they said, as if mocking him.

Vexed at their behaviour, he decided to go to them and ask them to leave. He quickly reached the corner where the voices had come from, but there was nobody there! He was puzzled. *How could this be possible*, he wondered. There was no way they could have left within that short span of time. In any case, he would have seen them, as there was only one entrance, which also served as the exit door, and it was near where he sat.

Just then ... 'Shhh!' someone whispered in his ear and laughed. The librarian ran out of the door as the laughter continued.

A number of such paranormal occurrences reported by the employees led to the executive committee of the local bar association to call a meeting specifically to mull over the evidence. It was decided that closed-circuit television cameras would be installed so they could find out what was going on. One of the grainy surveillance videos captured is the one that went viral on social media. It has plenty to satisfy believers—floating white orbs, flickering computer screens—and also, much to raise doubt among non-believers.

This was when Gaurav was called to investigate with his team. Raj, who is a Microsoft certified engineer, did the heavy lifting this time around. Gaurav knew he was the man for it and left much to be solved by him, so much so that he did not even get into the technical nitty-gritties.

'There was a period when people witnessed paranormal activity, but there was nothing to prove it. Now we have cameras, we can document whatever experience we have and our knowledge of understanding the paranormal is increasing,' Gaurav had said in one of his shows, around the time that Raj became a part of his team.

Raj analysed things for over two hours before informing him that the computers were scheduled for maintenance and were malfunctioning. But the EMF meters had certainly shown a spike during the evening, and so they decided to stay back at night. They would be accompanied by only Bhavesh Tyagi from the court.

'Saab, I'm a poor man. Why me?' he grumbled. But someone from the court had to be present with them.

The hotspots were ascertained on the basis of the cases

reported so far: the main library, one of the corridors, an office area and the small cyber library that can be seen in the viral video.

Tyagi served them some tea and snacks before they ventured out for what they had come to do—face the dead!

'Tyagi-ji, you have been here since 1993. Any unnatural deaths that you know of?' Raj asked him. He was a big believer in the fact that a lot could happen over tea.

Tyagi nodded and said, 'There were a few suicides that happened many years ago.' He told them that he had no clue why these people had taken that step. All he knew was that these lawyers were involved in a high-profile case that went awry in court.

The team began with the main library first, led by Gaurav who conducted the investigation in his trademark style. With their equipment in place, they walked slowly and covered the entire area, but there wasn't much to write home about. It was only around 11 p.m. that their EMF meters began spiking. That was when Tyagi re-joined them; he had left for a while to complete some work.

'Got anything?' he asked.

'It's begun,' Gaurav told the team, indicating the gradual spikes.

'Let's move to the corridor. But what makes this a hotspot?' Raj asked Tyagi.

Tyagi told him about an incident when he had gone to get tea for a senior officer and was crossing the open corridor. A man, who looked lost and worried, asked him where he could find one Mr Lalwani's office.

'Lalwani? There is nobody by that name here. Not to my knowledge,' he'd said.

'Not possible. Not possible. I have an appointment with him. It's important. He doesn't want to meet me, is it? Please tell him ...' he cried.

Tyagi, being the good-hearted simple man that he was, got embarrassed and really wanted to help him, but he knew there wasn't anyone called Lalwani there.

'What is the matter?' he asked. He wanted to console the man who seemed like he had lost a lot in life.

'Only he can save me and my family from bankruptcy. Please help me,' he said, crying even more.

'Tell me, when is the appointment today? Maybe you got the name wrong.'

'No, no. It's Lalwani itself. I met him last month and he promised to meet me today. Today! See, I have noted it in my diary too.'

The man dug into his dirty old bag and took out a battered diary, opened it and showed it to Tyagi.

It read: 17 December 1996.

'What kind of a joke is this?' Bhavesh Tyagi looked up at the man furiously, but there was nobody there in the broad daylight.

'It was painful for me, saab. Somehow, I have come across many of these terrifying incidents—more than anyone else here,' Tyagi told the IPS team.

'That's because you have been here for years,' Raj said, trying to cheer him up. But Tyagi seemed miserable recalling the traumatic experiences.

He showed the IPS team the way to the corridor and stayed behind them.

Raj switched on the EVF so that voice anomalies could be analysed later, and made sure he captured as many images as possible. Unfortunately, the video camera hadn't been functioning since the afternoon and there was no time to go back to the office and get another. Glitches do happen when it comes to anything technical.

Nothing unusual happened during the investigation, barring the EMF spikes.

'They don't want to communicate, it seems. But the place is haunted. We should come back here later. I'll give the details to Mr Sharma,' Gaurav told the team as they wrapped up for the night. He was not satisfied with the progress.

Tyagi bid them goodbye at the main gate and said with a smile, '*Jab aaoge, milte rahenge* (We will keep meeting whenever you are here).'

'Can we go to your home and close the findings tonight itself?' Gaurav asked Raj, who lived closer to the court than the others.

'Goes without saying,' he said.

Gaurav knew he wouldn't be able to sleep without analysing the evidence. He would arrive at a conclusion, go to the office, catch up with pending work, send the official mail to Raman Sharma and then go home to sleep. His team shared that passion for work as well. Also, this was an important case, and one very close to Gaurav. The IPS was the first professional paranormal team to have investigated a functional court—not only in India but in the world. The news was also covered by *The Washington Post*. It marked a new milestone for the IPS team as news of the investigation went viral around the world.

But not everything could be covered … not everything would be believed …

Soon the team was in Raj's place with strong coffee and some snacks to keep them going through the post-investigation stage.

Raj decided to go through the images he'd taken, while Gaurav took up the responsibility of listening to the audio anomalies very carefully, wanting to check if any entity was out there, trying to communicate with them.

'Look!' Raj said suddenly. He showed them the photographs he had taken while at the court. Tyagi was nowhere in them! And he had definitely been there with them during many of the instances when Raj had taken photographs.

Gaurav froze for a moment, but he had been pondering over the audio recording too. Tyagi had said a lot when they were together, but why couldn't he be heard? There were just slight disturbances in the audio whenever he spoke, and Gaurav recalled that a few times when he did that, the EVP meter had shown spikes!

'Call Mr Sharma! Now!' he said.

After they'd spoken to Sharma, he connected with Tyagi's family members and was informed that the old man had committed suicide in the late evening, in the court itself.

Raj sat down on the floor with a thud, completely blank, unsure how he was supposed to react. He had had a good conversation with the man during the day and had liked his simplicity. Gaurav had too. He had been a nice man. Why had he …

'Jab aaoge, milte rahenge.'

His smiling face would haunt the team for years to come.

Had he been so sad and terrified because of the years of paranormal experiences? Had his personal life been getting affected? Had he been so lonely that he couldn't share his feelings with anyone? Tyagi's reason for taking this course of action remains unknown.

'It's been quite some time. Over an hour or more, I think,' I said, looking at my watch.

'Let me call her,' Siddharth said and dialled Meghna's number. It wasn't reachable.

'Must be the rain,' he said and offered me some tea. I must have had at least six cups by then, but I wasn't complaining. The hot beverage, the weather outside and the true hair-raising stories were going well together.

'So, Gaurav had an arranged marriage?' I wanted to delve a little more into the individual and find out more about the man behind the image.

Siddharth nodded.

Ever since Gaurav had turned thirty, his parents had been going ballistic at his bachelor status. They wanted him to get married as soon as possible. As they would remind him, Gaurav was already going to school when his father was his age! They came from a community where marriages happened early, and it was believed to be in the best interests of everyone. His father was conservative about love marriages, but in any case Gaurav didn't have a girl in his life. One needs time for a relationship, and his work demanded that he travel often to various places. Though he was a known personality by this time, his profession was no child's play, and he had asked his father to intimate the repercussions to every woman they ever had in mind for him. The search had been on for a few months. Gaurav had met a few of the women too, but nothing had clicked.

'The best part is that I have promised my parents like a good Indian boy that I will marry a girl of their choice. So they keep looking for girls, but when a girl's parents hear about what I do, they run away as if I am some ghost! There is another benefit of not getting married. I can do my research whenever I want,' he joked once and his team had a good laugh.

Then, he met Arya. She was the complete opposite of Gaurav. While he was a quiet, reserved person, she was vivacious and talkative. Anything he did was after a lot of thought, while she was impulsive. He took time to open up and communicate; she spoke her mind without thinking twice. There was an instant connection between the two from the first time they met. A certain kind of curiosity is the reason behind love that blossoms between two people poles apart from each other. Over the next few days after their first meeting at Arya's home, they found themselves catching up whenever possible so they could get to know each other better.

Gaurav was focusing more on his personal life, but that did not mean he had lost focus on his profession. However, he did try to travel less frequently. Arya wasn't too keen on Gaurav's field and wanted him to do something more concrete, something more stable, something safe. Perhaps a corporate job. But Gaurav was definitely not made for that. She stood by him and adjusted a lot, trying her best to make things work while also motivating him at times.

They got married on 28 January 2016. At first things went smoothly, but soon Arya realised the demands of Gaurav's profession. Though he had cut down on travelling outside Delhi NCR, there were so many cases in the city itself. And most of these cases had to be investigated at night. This meant Gaurav would often return home in the early morning, when Arya would have to leave for her office. Arya again asked Gaurav to contemplate changing his profession, but he was adamant he wouldn't, and couldn't as well.

'Arya, please understand. This is what I can do. This is what I love to do! Also, it's too late for a switch in career,' he told her patiently one day.

'Gaurav, Gaurav. Don't make this difficult, please,' she sobbed.

'I'm adjusting, no? I'll stop the night visits too. Okay?'

'It's not only about that, Gaurav. It's about your profession. It's not a job. You know that, right?'

'For me it is. Let's not argue about this, Arya.'

His parents wanted him to begin a new life too. They felt it was an unstable and hazardous work he was into, and, to add to their woes, it wasn't profitable. Only Gaurav knew how he was managing to run it.

It was difficult running the show with not much inflow of money, but when he was asked what he got from it, Gaurav had stated, 'I never started this work for any rewards. I never realised that my work can get so huge that it will make me one of the most sought-after investigators in the world. A lot of people told me when I began that I was on a wrong path and I was wasting my life in a field that no one cares about. But today, after doing four big television shows in India and a couple of them internationally which aired in almost forty countries, I feel no less than an international TV star; plus, the respect is surplus. I was told that I am the only resident Indian to be appearing on television in more than thirty countries and now on American TV—that too on a big network like SyFy. But the most rewarding thing in this field is when people come to me with a satisfied face and a smile telling me how I have helped them and improved their lives or how I have made them fearless.'

Arya did support him at times, visiting certain locations with him while he was at work, but it was clear that she would have preferred that he spend more time with her.

Gaurav was probably not at peace in his personal life in the last few months before his death, but he never let that affect his professional duties. Nor did he ever discuss his problems with anyone, not till a personal trip to Lansdowne. Raj and Siddharth had accompanied Gaurav, Arya and a few other mutual friends there for a short weekend holiday.

In the evening, they organised a barbeque in the backyard of the hotel and they were all having a good time when suddenly they saw Arya screaming at Gaurav, and then they both left the venue, leaving everyone there asking what had happened in hushed tones. It was only later that night that Gaurav opened up to Raj about a few of his personal issues. Siddharth had gone to sleep by then.

NINE

LLOYD HAUNTING—A DOG'S SPIRIT

We, at the Indian Paranormal Society, see spirits as other human beings who are lost, confused or misguided and not as something that can play with your fate or something that can kill you. There is no single proof on this earth that shows that a person has been killed by a spirit. People often get killed or destroyed due to their own fear and belief.

— GAURAV TIWARI

Summer 2009

Nilanjan Kanjilal had moved from Kolkata to Bangalore with his wife, Verona, due to better prospects in his IT career. An official transfer meant the relocation expenses would be borne by the employer. The move happened so quickly, though, that Nilanjan had no time to search for a rented apartment before they shifted. They decided to stay at a hotel for a week or two till they found a place to reside. Before they left, Verona had been clear that she wanted their furniture transported to the city.

'We can search for a furnished apartment,' Nilanjan had suggested.

'No way, Nilu! I want our stuff there. Let's send it through a packer and mover. It will take a week or more for them to deliver, and we will surely find a place by then,' Verona had been firm.

When they reached Bangalore, they checked into a five-star hotel. Nilanjan would head to his office in the early morning and be back by afternoon, and then the couple would go house-hunting. Verona, being very particular, rejected many of Nilanjan's choices. Then they realised there was just no time left. The furniture would be delivered in a day, so they had to find an apartment on priority.

'Don't be choosy!' Nilanjan reminded Verona before entering the last place the broker had to show them.

It wasn't a high-rise but a house with three storeys; the third and first floors were already rented out. A square-grey building, with narrow windows in straight rows, there was nothing about it in the least picturesque or attractive, yet, to Verona, there was something about it that was fascinating.

They ignored a lot of what they saw. In one of the rooms, there was a burnt mattress, and some spots in a few corners looked as if they'd been burnt as well. When asked, the owner and broker told them that the previous tenant smoked a lot and the room had caught fire one day. The owner had then asked him to leave the house.

The very next day, Nilanjan and Verona moved in and their furniture was delivered there. And a week later, Lloyd joined them.

Lloyd—their lovely dog, a German shepherd. Nilanjan had gifted Verona this bundle of joy a few years ago on their first wedding anniversary. Lloyd was five now. A handsome boy who had been Verona's constant companion. He had such an expressive look about him—you could tell when he was puzzled, excited or serious, all those emotions that are so similar to ours. He was Verona's hot-water bottle in the middle of the night when Nilanjan had late work shifts, and the welcome party when he came home.

Nilanjan's office wasn't too far away from where they lived, but the work pressure was immense. Long working hours and night shifts became the norm within a few days, leaving Verona alone much of the time—but at least she had Lloyd with her. She had known this was bound to happen. With bigger responsibilities come less personal time! So, in a way, she had been mentally prepared. But not for what was in store for them …

One afternoon, Verona was taking a nap in the bedroom when a knock woke her up. But it didn't come from the front door. She knew that, but to be sure, she went to the main door to check. She was right. There was nobody there. Perhaps she had imagined that she'd heard it, she thought. Back in bed, closing her eyes, she tried to get back to sleep when she heard it again.

KNOCK! KNOCK!

Twice! It had come from the room itself! It had come from … from the window!

Who could it be now? Was it someone who was repairing something and was on a ladder? Perhaps the person needed something.

It came again. Thrice now. Louder. Clearer.

Verona drew open the curtain but there was nobody there.

KNOCK! KNOCK!

It came again! Right from there itself!

Verona screamed and rushed downstairs with Lloyd. She called Nilanjan and explained what had happened.

'Come early! Just come!' she told him, and spent the evening at a neighbour's place.

'There is a graveyard here!' she told Nilanjan as soon as he returned. 'There!' She pointed to the graveyard she had only spotted when her neighbour had told her about it.

The graveyard was no more than a series of wooden crosses of random sizes stuck in the grassy loam. Most of them were painted white and bore a scribbled name and date. But it was shocking for the couple that it was so close to where they were staying. Neither of them had noticed it, and neither the owner nor the broker had informed them about it. Yes, there was an option; they could move to another place, but it would involve relocation expenses from their own pocket, and more importantly, the hassle of trying to find another apartment. They decided to give it some time.

The next Sunday, both Nilanjan and Verona were at home watching television when Lloyd started barking all of a sudden. He seemed terrified of something, very terrified! It was after this that a string of very weird incidents began to happen. Strange noises came from somewhere at night, somewhere in the house itself, but they could never make out from where. Sometimes they found the fridge door wide open when they woke up in the morning. Things were misplaced, other things were lost, there was a crack in the large mirror in the bedroom one morning—and this was just the beginning.

One night, Nilanjan woke up with a jolt to realise that someone had pulled his blanket down while he was asleep. Then he heard those noises again—as if someone was in a lot of hurry. It was coming from the kitchen. Without waking Verona up, he decided to check it himself. He walked towards the kitchen and saw from a distance that the lights were on. His mind was more focused on his own footsteps, which seemed to be echoing. As he reached ...

'Darling, would you like to have a cup of tea?' Verona asked him.

'What ... You were in the bedroom ... What are you ...' Nilanjan was so puzzled that he couldn't find the words to express his feelings.

'What are you saying? I'm here. See. It's me!' Verona smiled.

'Tea now? It's 2.30 in the morning, Ver-Verona!' Nilanjan stood there, baffled. He had been so sure that he had felt his wife next to him a few seconds ago in the bedroom.

'So?' She came closer to Nilanjan.

'Nilanjan ...' Verona's voice came from behind, and Nilanjan turned around to see her standing where he had been a couple of minutes back!

'What the ...' Nilanjan trembled and walked back a few steps.

'Who are you talking to?' Verona asked, walking up to him.

'Look ...' Nilanjan turned around, but there was nobody there.

The kettle was on.

'You were making tea? Now?' Verona asked Nilanjan, who shook with fear from what he had just witnessed.

Over the next few days, Lloyd seemed to become very weak and kept to himself. He wasn't hungry or thirsty. This was clearly not the age for such behaviour and Verona took him to a vet, who examined him thoroughly and concluded there was nothing wrong with him. But their best friend continued to get more weak and began behaving very strangely. He would bark for no reason, which sounded more like whining as he had no energy. It was depressing to see him spend all his time in one corner of the house from where he refused to move.

One night, his barks woke up both Nilanjan and Verona. It had been a while since they had heard him yap so loudly. Verona rushed to see what was wrong with her fur boy but she was too late. He was no more. Lloyd lay in the hall, utterly still and more than slightly frozen. At first glance, the cause wasn't apparent, but the chances of it being natural were many. They both had seen it coming but hadn't wanted to accept it at a subconscious level. The next day, Lloyd was buried along with his belongings, which included a collar with a small bell, gifted to him on his last birthday. For the couple, life came to a standstill. They cried and cried, and then Verona cried a little more.

It would be difficult to get over Lloyd's death, they both knew. His presence was missed the second they stepped into the house after his funeral.

'We should move to another place, Verona. We should,' Nilanjan told her a few days before an official trip to Pune.

'No, Nilanjan. Relocating is such a pain. What we can do is get a priest to bless the house.'

'No, Verona. I have a better idea.'

'And what's that?'

'Gaurav Tiwari,' he said.

Gaurav happened to be in Bangalore for some other work when he received a call from Nilanjan, who had got his number through a reference. The IPS was still in its nascent stages back then, and Gaurav was busy doing the groundwork himself. He travelled to various cities and towns to build a team and network with respect to his vision, and was in Bangalore for the same reason. After chatting with Nilanjan, it was decided that he would pay them a visit on Sunday when Nilanjan would be home too.

On Sunday morning, Verona was preparing breakfast while Nilanjan was on a call with his parents when …

They heard the chiming of a bell … just like they used to hear when Lloyd walked, ran or simply moved in the house. It was that loud! It was the same sound! They could not have been mistaken.

It had come from the hall, as if Lloyd was walking there. But how could that be possible? The chiming stopped for a few seconds when Nilanjan and Verona reached the hall, stupefied as well as frightened. Lloyd's presence … they could feel it! It felt like he was there, looking at both of them. Then they heard the chiming again. It was coming from the middle of the hall and seemed to be getting closer to where they stood; it came nearer with every breath till they could sense someone very close to them.

'L-Lloyd …' Verona whispered.

There was no response. The chiming stopped too.

Gaurav arrived at their place in the afternoon.

'Hi!' he greeted them with a wide smile at the door.

Nilanjan and Verona tried hard to smile but weren't in the right frame of mind. Gaurav understood what they must be going through.

'Who is the owner?' he asked after listening to what had been transpiring in the house.

'Sainath Hebbar. He lives nearby,' Nilanjan replied.

'Please ask him to come over in the next ten minutes,' Gaurav said, and then began checking all the rooms. He was carrying an EMF meter with him. He hadn't met Raj yet, at this point.

'So, that's the graveyard?' He pointed to the place from the balcony after conducting an EVP session in one of the rooms. 'Guys, many times spirits are intelligent and they know they can communicate with you or respond to you. I have got a few intelligent responses here. When is Mr Hebbar …'

'Yes, yes. Gaurav, Mr Hebbar is here,' Verona informed him as she went to the front door and opened it.

'Sainath Hebbar. I'm the—' the owner began to introduce himself.

'Sorry. No time for introductions,' Gaurav said, gesturing for him to come in. 'I'll get straight to the point, Mr Hebbar. What happened here?' Gaurav demanded.

'Who are you?' Hebbar clearly wasn't happy about the treatment on his own property.

'Doesn't matter.' Gaurav may have sounded a little rude, but that wasn't his intention. He just wanted answers, quickly.

'Gaurav, he is the owner of this …' Nilanjan wanted to request Gaurav to be a little gentle.

'I know, Nilanjan. But what he and the broker did was wrong. They should have divulged everything.'

'Agreed. They should have told us that there is a graveyard near the place. We didn't notice it either.'

'It's … it's not just about the graveyard, Nilanjan. This place is more than that,' Gaurav said. 'You owe us an explanation, Mr Hebbar. I'm investigating this place and it's needed for documentation.'

Hebbar had understood by now that the man who had been nearly lashing out at him had a purpose and was probably influential too. It would be better to tell him everything.

'Nilanjan … I lied …' he said and broke down.

He revealed that the previous tenant had other problems apart from smoking, and they were certainly graver than taking just a puff. The tenant had been from a very wealthy family in Ooty and was in Bangalore for his post-graduation. But all he did was drink the whole day. He used to do drugs too, and Hebbar later found out that prostitutes would stay over at the apartment. He had decided to warn his tenant.

'The next time I hear or see anything that goes against you, I'll kick you out of here,' he snarled at the boy half his age.

But the guy wouldn't pay heed to his warning. They learnt later that he had major problems with his family, and his father was on the verge of disowning him. One night, Hebbar was on the road, smoking, when he saw a girl leaving the place as furtively as she could.

'Son of a ...' He threw the cigarette and rushed up to confront the boy.

'I'll throw him out tonight itself,' he said as he entered the house. The door was wide open. His tenant had probably not closed it after the girl left.

Hebbar searched for him like a mad wolf on the prowl till he noticed smoke in the bedroom. He hurried there and saw that the boy had set himself on fire! Blank for a moment and not sure what he could do, he ran to the washroom. The buckets were empty. He had to fill them up quickly. Within the room, the fire spread with ease, turning the once pretty floor into a maze of flames. Black smoke billowed. Hebbar began choking as the sound of the crackling fire became clearer with every second he lost in filling the buckets. Just then, he noticed a pipe in the corner of the washroom, which he recalled he had bought a year ago for the lawn.

He shouted in joy, fixed it to the tap and rushed out to the room. He pointed the nozzle of the pipe and water gushed out of it. He tried hard, really hard, but couldn't save the boy. He was declared dead even before reaching the hospital. His parents were informed and the police was involved for a few days till they concluded it was a case of death by suicide. The boy had been high on drugs, they said. There'd been a break up sometime back, and he hadn't been able to handle it.

Hebbar said the boy's parents had refused to take their son's body, and so he had been buried in the graveyard nearby, with the police's permission.

'Hmm. Nilanjan, this place has never been good, really. But it is this boy's spirit that has been haunting you guys.' Gaurav had determined this within a few minutes of entering the house, even before Hebbar's confession.

Gaurav began a procedure to cleanse the house and asked Hebbar to leave.

'This will take a few hours,' he said and got to work.

It was a little past noon then.

Gaurav had nearly completed what was necessary for the couple to continue living there.

Bang!

There was someone at the door! The knocks got louder. Someone was furious, furious at what was going on inside the house. Gaurav's EMF meter documented a high spike, indicating the presence of a strong entity.

'Get out of here!' he shouted. He knew this spirit was in no mood for a proper discussion. It was twisted and harmful.

Bang! Bang! Bang!

Fear stifled Nilanjan and Verona like a pillow over their mouths and noses. Had Gaurav not been there, what would they have done?

The entity continued to hit the door with force.

'What do you want?' Gaurav asked, his EMF meter on the highest spike.

No answer. Just the banging.

Then they all heard another sound in the midst of the horror. The chiming of a bell! This time it was accompanied by the sound of a dog running and panting … as if Lloyd was running towards the door. And the banging stopped. Nilanjan and Verona looked at each other, totally bewildered.

A few minutes later, the EMF meter normalised, indicating no paranormal activity at the time. Gaurav drank a glass of water and asked them while packing his bag, 'What was your dog's name?'

'Lloyd,' they said at the same time.

Gaurav smiled.

'I love dogs.'

Then, after a brief pause, he concluded, 'You need not worry. Lloyd is here, protecting you from any evil spirit that might want to trouble you.'

Verona's eyes filled with tears. She looked toward the wall where they had hung Lloyd's photograph. She recalled how difficult it had been for her to get him to pose for this one.

'Lloyd, I'll give you double the treat!' she had bribed him and kissed his wet nose. Lloyd had jumped and hugged her before they had gone ahead and clicked it.

'Our best friend, Lloyd.' Nilanjan embraced her warmly, trying to console her.

'I'll be a call away,' Gaurav said and left.

TEN

ARADALE ASYLUM WITH THE HAUNTING: AUSTRALIA TEAM

To fight the evil outside in the world, you must first fight the evil inside yourself.

— GAURAV TIWARI

December 1997

David woke up, his eyes slowly opening to focus on the naked bulb above. He was dimly aware of his body being rigid and straight—no movement was possible. Lifting his head, he could see thick straps over his arms and legs. Saliva pooled in the back of his throat and he swallowed, panicking. He twisted his limbs, turning them, feeling the friction of the fabric against his skin. He realised he was in a hospital, though he couldn't recall why he was there, or when he had arrived. The last he remembered, he had found out his wife had been cheating on him. It was all blank after that. He had no clue how much time had passed since that moment.

'Is anyone here?' he called out. His voice echoed in the corridor just outside the room.

There was nobody there. But someone must have brought him in. Was this a nightmare? David bit his tongue. It hurt. No, it wasn't a dream; he was awake.

He tried but couldn't get out of the bindings. He tried harder, using all his strength, and then realised that it was impossible. Also that he felt weak, really very weak. Not too many good things had happened since the moment he had caught his wife red-handed. He had trusted her so much, loved her so much! And she had slept with his own cousin? Where had he gone wrong in the relationship? So many thoughts bothered him, but he knew it wasn't the right time for that. For now he had to get out of this damned dirty place!

'Anyone?' he shouted at the top of his voice, but it wasn't loud, he felt.

Just then, he heard footsteps approaching. They echoed sharply down the corridor, sounding overly loud, like the booming heartbeat of a condemned prisoner.

A lady, probably in her early thirties, walked in and greeted David with a smile. 'Welcome to Ararat Lunatic Asylum,' she said.

'Why am I here? Who are you?' David studied her. She was clearly a nurse, from her attire, and he felt rather silly asking her that question.

'I'm Nurse Kerry. I'm the head nurse here. I'll be taking care of you while you are here,' she said.

'But why the fuck am I here?' David growled.

'Hmm, let's see.' Nurse Kerry opened the file that was on a table in the room.

'You killed your wife and went insane,' she said.

'No! You are lying, Nurse. That can't be! I could not have killed my wife. I love her so much!' he screamed, mostly because, somewhere in his subconscious, he knew it was the truth.

'Yes, you must have loved her. Crimes of passion are dangerous, David. But you have to recover. Let me assure you that this is the right place for that. But you have to first begin with acceptance ... accepting the truth,' she said patiently, while David howled in pain and misery. Was he a criminal now, and an insane one at that? David Wilson was one of the big names in Melbourne when it came to lawyers. So much respect, so much fame, so much money, so much more he could be! But now he was a mad man who had killed his wife in a fit of rage. And this was his new home now.

'Nurse, I don't want to be here ...' David sobbed, realising the repercussions of the crime he had committed.

'What's done is done, David. But you will be fine here. This place is great ...'

Another nurse walked in.

'The doctor will be here shortly,' she said.

David looked at her and asked Nurse Kerry, 'Is she your subordinate?'

Nurse Kerry smiled.

'Who ... who are you talking to?' The other nurse gaped at him.

'Can't you see your superior here?' he asked, pointing. All she could see was him pointing towards the wall.

'Nurse Kerry, tell her!' he screeched.

'They can't see me unless I want them to. I'm here for my patients.' Nurse Kerry's eyes twinkled and then she disappeared, leaving the new patient at Aradale Mental Hospital petrified.

'She is long dead … she died many years ago,' the nurse told him, and decided to talk to her superiors about this incident, one of the many that the place was infamous for.

August 2013

Gaurav Tiwari was a name to reckon with by now in India. He was very occupied with the IPS at this point, and it was difficult for him to take up cases abroad. But he had always wanted to investigate a mental asylum and hadn't had a chance to do so yet. Moreover, his *Haunting: Australia* team members wanted to catch up with each other. It had been a few years now!

Aradale Mental Hospital is located in Ararat, a city two hours from Melbourne. Built in the 1860s, the hospital was originally known as the Ararat Lunatic Asylum. In Ararat, it is referred to as the 'asylum', as if it were a place of refuge; it was anything but. It was a place for people no one knew what to do with, and they were put there only to be forgotten by the wider world. It was a prison for the sick. They took your dignity along with your clothes, talked to you as if you were a challenged child, and fed you terrible food in small portions. And then they watched you, recording any negative emotions and praising dull and passive behaviour. The asylum was no place to seek asylum, not in the true sense of the term. It should have been a place of refuge from the storms that hurt the mind, a place of care and sanctuary, a place where you could be welcomed until the entire self was soothed, an anchor in a hurricane. In truth, the 'asylum' would have been more aptly named as a house of torture, for the removal of all hope. The bare walls and bare floors were reflections of what the place really was, as if the building itself was trying to tell the staff what they had built and perpetuated. Then there were the windowless rooms, the lack of real light, the doors without handles. It was the world's most obvious constructed metaphor for emotional indifference.

A part of the hospital is now a college campus and it is no longer a psychiatric facility—it used to be Australia's largest at one time. Now it has come to be known as something else: Australia's most haunted asylum. The psychiatric hospital, which functioned from 1865 until 1998, was known for its poor conditions and Victorian approach to medical health. Electro-convulsive therapy and trans-orbital lobotomies were common practices, from which not even children were excluded. It's no wonder that paranormal enthusiasts are drawn to the vast labyrinthine buildings; the more the number of unhappy deaths, the more scope to investigate and know the unknown. The place has been the subject of multiple investigations, including one that was televised, where investigators claim to have seen a face in one of the cells. There have been reports of shadowy figures in the hallway, and people getting scratched too. The erstwhile hospital also had a morgue where a college student once saw a lady walk in and disappear. There were also incidents of something there pushing them back downstairs.

Ian Lawman, Ray Jorden, Allen Tiller, Robb Demarest, Rayleen Kable and Gaurav Tiwari flew to Melbourne together. They drove to Ararat from the airport and checked into a motel as it was late night. The plan was simple—sleep till afternoon and begin the investigation in the late evening.

'What exactly happened here over the many decades?' Gaurav asked the team while at dinner.

'Torture. A lot of it to a lot of people,' Ian said.

'Thirteen thousand or more, to be precise,' Robb added.

They reached the asylum a little before seven in the evening the next day so that they would have enough time to check it out properly.

'Where do we start?' Allen asked.

'This place … it's like a buffet for horror enthusiasts. No wonder there is a ghost tour too, arranged every Friday and Saturday,' Rayleen said. She had read and heard about the place and, like Gaurav, she was excited because it was on the list of haunted destinations left for her to explore.

'No plan as such this time. Let's just go in for the kill, mates.' Gaurav smiled and took out the equipment he would be using.

When the facility was functioning, men and women who were considered suicidal and violent were kept on the second floor. There was this particular room there that left visitors with feelings of nausea and terror and put them in trance-like states. Gaurav decided to cover that area himself.

'Hi, anyone here?' he greeted the spirits around as he reached the biggest hotspot for paranormal activities in the asylum. He was wheelchair-bound at this time because he had met with an accident earlier. He had decided to complete the *Haunting: Australia* tour even with the challenges of a leg in a cast.

The EMF meter spiked. These were entities that wouldn't shy away from contact.

'Great! Show yourself.'

He heard footsteps, as if someone were walking around him in a circle, looking at him while on the move. Gaurav could sense it, the presence as well as the intent. Not a good place to be in, he felt.

Taking out his full-spectrum camera, he joked, 'Okay, smile please,' and began taking photographs.

The footsteps stopped and then he saw a lady walk into one of the rooms on the floor. From her attire, he could make out she was a nurse. Nurse Kerry? She was known to haunt the wards and was thought to be continuing her duties, looking out for her former patients in the afterlife. Her ghost has been seen by many and heard by even more. There had been many reports of hearing the disembodied click of a woman's high heels throughout the empty ward, as well as the soft sounds of a woman's voice, something that Kerry was known for when alive. But most of the other spirits to roam Aradale were not as friendly as Nurse Kerry. Gaurav was exactly where the most dangerous patients used to be kept.

He followed the nurse to the room, continuing to take photographs while also switching on the EVP in order to record voice anomalies.

'Madam …' he said softly, a few inches behind her in the dark room.

'You shouldn't be here,' she whispered and vanished.

'Get out of my room!' a man's yell startled Gaurav. He flashed his flashlight around, but apart from an old broken bed, there was nothing there.

The main door slammed shut and then opened with a loud bang. The patient who lived there in the afterlife didn't like to be disturbed. He might have been another infamous ghost, that of Gary Webb. It was said that he had mutilated his body over seventy times and didn't like people coming to his room. Gaurav took a few more photographs, focusing his camera on the bed, and then left the room.

This place is one of the most disquieting I've visited so far, he thought.

The footsteps could be heard again … someone walking around him—swift but heavy footsteps.

'Is there something you want to tell me?' Gaurav checked if his EVP was on.

The footsteps got louder … louder … even louder …

Then they stopped.

'Anyone here?' Gaurav looked around and shone his flashlight in all the corners.

'Leave!' someone whispered in his ear.

The only thing these spirits wanted to tell him was that he should leave. The ghosts of Aradale didn't like interference.

'Got anything?' Robb asked Gaurav when they all met in a separate building, outside the main one.

'Nurse Kerry!' He showed them one of the photographs he had taken. There it was! An apparition of a woman in a nurse's attire, her head tilted to her left.

'Fabulous!' They all hugged Gaurav.

'Thanks, thanks! What next?'

'This, of course!' Rayleen opened the door to the morgue.

'So, who is up for the challenge?' Ian smiled and looked at everyone, pointing to the chiller—a cold steel slab where thousands of bodies had lain over years and decades.

'Me!' It was Gaurav. 'What? Don't stare at me like that! I've always wanted to do this,' he said and got ready.

Ian stood guard outside the morgue while the others left to explore other areas. A video camera was placed outside the chiller. Initially, Ray was supposed to take on this challenge, but he had got a little nervous. Gaurav was gung-ho about it though, and didn't think twice. Lying on the steel slab, he placed his head on a block while holding another video camera to record whatever would happen inside.

'You tell me when you are ready,' Ian said.

'All right, I am!' Gaurav smiled as Ian pushed the chiller in and closed it.

Finding himself confined in a space normally reserved for the dead, Gaurav observed the chiller.

I'm all alone. It stinks bad, he thought while shooting the experience live. *I'm just afraid that I might sleep here. It's so cosy here*, he continued talking to himself.

Knowledge cancelled fear, for Gaurav. Talking to himself solved the purpose too, at times!

It was close to thirty minutes that Ian waited outside, a little apprehensive about the decision. Ian didn't want to lose a dear friend. The place was terrible—he could sense it.

Gaurav is great at mind control. No wonder he could take up this big challenge, he told himself. He went in and opened the chiller.

'Phew! I was scared for you!' Ian hugged Gaurav tightly.

'But I had a great time!'

'How do you say it in Hindi ... *Kuch ... kuch ...?*' Ian had an interest in the language and often watched Hindi movies.

'*Kuch hua*, you mean?'

'Yeah, yeah!'

'Nope! Nothing that I can boast about.' Gaurav laughed. 'I have spent a lot of nights in places in India where there were rumours that whoever goes there doesn't survive the night. The chiller was nothing,' he added.

'Let's still play the two cameras and check.' Ian was hopeful. And he was right to be so. They had captured the voice of a young girl, someone who seemed to be in a lot of pain.

'Someone here wants to talk ... Little girl?' Gaurav called out, trying to communicate with the entity.

But there was no response.

Regardless, the team arrived at the conclusion that the abandoned Aradale Mental Hospital was one of the most haunted places they had investigated.

Meghna recalled a fun conversation with Gaurav when he told them about his experience at Aradale during one of his visits to Mumbai.

'What was going on in your mind when you were in there, in that chiller?' Meghna had asked.

'Ah, it was my little trick to catch up on some sleep,' he said and smiled.

His team laughed out loud.

'Dinner?' Meghna asked Abhirup and Siddharth. She had returned sometime back.

'Yes, please, I'm hungry,' I said. As we ate, I asked, 'Did any of the *Haunting: Australia* team members come to India and join you guys for a case?'

'Yes, yes. Of course. They were very close to Gaurav and treated him like a younger brother. And they all love India. Robb knew him much before the others, but once they all met, they just clicked,' Meghna said.

'Hmm … it just struck me that we haven't spoken about Bhangarh so far! That's supposedly the most haunted location in India, right?'

'It's not!'

'What? Really?'

'Not as per Gaurav sir, and he went there many times,' Siddharth confirmed.

December 2012

The first investigation of Bhangarh Fort by any paranormal professional was conducted by Gaurav Tiwari. He was really excited as the team drove up to the fort in Alwar district in Rajasthan, from the Sariska Tiger Reserve, passing by Ajabgarh Fort. Entry in Bhangarh is restricted after sunset, but they had got special permission for this investigation. Gaurav and his team would begin their work only after 8 p.m. Gaurav did tell people later that the drive to Bhangarh was eerie. They passed through a village which was ostensibly uninhabited. The road thereon was lined with the ruins of once-beautiful havelis. Children were seated in front of intricately carved wooden doors that had large rusted locks. It was a lonely, lonely place.

The fort was built by Raja Bhagwant Singh, the Kachwaha ruler of Amber, for his younger son Madho Singh, in AD 1573. One of the stories surrounding the fort is that an evil tantric tried to use black magic to make a beautiful princess, Ratnavati, fall in love with him. However, the princess found out about his ploy. She threw the oil that contained the spell on a boulder, and that rock crushed and killed the tantric. Before he died, the tantric apparently cursed the entire town of Bhangarh, saying that it too would be desolate, like he was.

Another legend revolves around a hermit who had cursed that if any house built in the fort was taller than his own and if its shadow fell on his, it would lead to the destruction of Bhangarh.

Gaurav knew this was a big investigation; he wanted to see if there was any truth behind the stories of Bhangarh being the most haunted place in India. But he was thoroughly disappointed. According to him, Bhangarh is not at all haunted. He also said that there were no djinns in the structure called jinn ki gufa, cave of the djinns, in the fort. Till date it is worshipped by people who believe that they will receive something if they pray to the djinns there. Everyone was surprised after Gaurav's declarations—and quite obviously so, because it's human nature to believe what we are fed over the years. So when Gaurav talked about it in his interviews, he was trolled a lot, especially by people with commercial motives—those who exploit Bhangarh and want to draw visitors there by cooking up more ghost stories.

There was pressure on Gaurav to change his statement, to revisit the place and say he was wrong about his conclusions during his first trip. There were death threats too, to him as well as a few team members. But Gaurav stuck to the truth. He busted the rumours surrounding the place.

In his blog, Gaurav wrote that superstition is very prevalent in the area and nearby villages. That is why, he said, villagers—themselves being afraid of spirits—stopped outsiders from visiting the Bhangarh ruins after dark.

ELEVEN

MUKESH MILLS

Indian Paranormal Society is a professional association of dedicated researchers, parapsychologists and enthusiasts focused on researching and understanding the human condition through the scientific study of aerial, anomalous and psychical phenomena, its reality and its effect on humanity. When we investigate, we try to find out the real reason behind the haunting.

— GAURAV TIWARI

October 2007

It was actor Reema Asthana's first horror movie, and now that she was making the transition from being just a pretty face romanced by superstars on screen to doing more challenging roles, she was thoroughly excited about the shoot. A part of it was to happen in Mukesh Mills, which is in Colaba, Mumbai. The mill—which was built in the 1870s—was abruptly closed after a terrible fire in 1982, in which workers lost their lives. The exact cause of the fire remains unknown. After the tragedy, the place remained abandoned till now, when this eerie-looking property caught the fancy of a few filmmakers in the Hindi film industry.

The director had explained the scene to Reema, who was a little more concerned about how she would look than what she would be enacting.

'A little touch up here, please,' she told her make-up artist, indicating her eyes.

'Madam, keep it natural. In this scene you are supposed to be frightened, not pretty,' the director reminded her, thinking what a wrong choice she was for the role.

'Damn! I had told the producer to approach Urmila. She is such a fantastic actress, and horror comes to her easily. I'm telling you, Patil. If this movie bombs, it will be because of this lady,' he told his assistant during a smoke break before beginning his work.

'It's so hot in here,' Reema complained as she left her make-up van.

'That blink-and-miss cameo in the last Yash Raj film is the reason behind her tantrums, I tell you, Patil,' the director grumbled and quickly changed the tone of his voice the next second.

'Donny, *madam ke liye kucch thanda laao jaldi* (Bring a cold drink for madam),' he ordered the boy who ran errands for the crew.

Reema sipped her cola as everyone waited for her.

'Mohan-ji, I'm ready. Say one, two, three. Okay?' she giggled.

'One. Two. Three,' the director said with zero enthusiasm, and it showed on his face.

Blank! She was blank! The director was losing his patience now. He raised his voice. 'Reema, you need to look frightened!'

'Leave this place now.' It was a male voice, but it was coming from Reema, her head bent down.

'Yes?' Mohan thought it must be another tantrum.

'Yes. You heard right. Get out!' Reema looked up and stared at Mohan; her eyes were red and gleaming. Evil eyes. And the smile on her face ... it was blood-curdling. 'Didn't you hear? Get out!' the male voice screamed from within her. Reema's body began shooing away people as if they had trespassed on a property belonging to her and she was furious.

A few seconds later, some kind of a realisation dawned on her. It showed on her face—from evil to anger to blankness to confusion. Why was everyone staring at her? Had she done something wrong? She couldn't even recall what had happened in the last one minute or so. She had been standing close to the director's chair and asking him to start rolling. But now she was a little far away from there— when had she walked there?

The crew packed up and never returned.

December 2014

With many cases, Gaurav would proactively visit a location first and then involve the media for the subsequent visits. It was the news channels that would then take the necessary permissions to investigate a property. Gaurav had invited Robb Demarest to India for this case, and Robb was more than happy to visit. It would be his first time in the country.

'Show me the Taj Mahal!' he joked before booking the flight ticket.

Siddharth joined the two veterans; it helped that he was a Mumbaikar. Zee News would be covering the investigation—one news anchor and two crew members.

'What's the story behind this place?' Robb asked Siddharth, who was in awe and happy just to be spending time with the two experts. It was a great opportunity for him.

'It was built by someone called Muljibhai Madhvani in the 1870s. It was the only mill at the time, and was built in Colaba with private docks so that ships could easily unload and load stuff,' Siddharth said.

Meanwhile, Gaurav was on the phone with the reporter from Zee News. 'Where have you reached?' he asked. He had ensured that they themselves had reached the venue ten minutes before 8 p.m., which was the time for the meeting.

'Sir, Mumbai traffic. Please understand. We should be there in twenty minutes or so,' the reporter answered.

'*Ameer log* (Rich people)! Are they nuts? At peak time, they take the road? They could have easily taken a train and reached by now. It wouldn't even have been crowded as it's against rush hour traffic now,' Siddharth said to Gaurav while Robb went to a nearby shop to buy cigarettes.

'Leave it. We are on time. That's what matters,' Gaurav said calmly.

Gaurav went up to the watchman seated there to strike up a conversation. He asked him about the stories that had been doing the rounds about Mukesh Mills, and the watchman, Kalpesh, said he believed it was haunted too. He shared his own experience.

A few days ago, like he did daily, Kalpesh was closing the gates of the mills as he stepped out of the property. Just then, he heard some music coming from inside the premises. There had been no film shooting that day, and anyway, it was night, and even people from the movies were not allowed then.

'*Koi hai* (Is there anyone inside)?' Kalpesh's voice echoed.

There was no response. The music stopped too. Kalpesh peeked into the premises to see someone smoking there. He had the fright of his life as he was sure there was nobody inside! Kalpesh left the place immediately and spent the night on the opposite pavement; as scared as he was, he did not want to neglect his duty.

Robb offered Kalpesh a cigarette, not understanding what he was saying, but fear is a universal feeling and it showed on his face.

'You need this,' he said and patted Kalpesh on his back. He asked Gaurav to translate what he'd said.

'I've heard another story,' Siddharth said after Gaurav was done.

A few months ago, a renowned director was shooting a horror movie with children in Mukesh Mills. One of the young actors, a ten-year-old girl who was accompanied by her father, lost her way from the make-up room to the location and wasn't to be seen anywhere for a few minutes. A crew member searched for her, found and brought her to the director.

'Where were you?' the director asked the girl.

'The uncle with the white hat took me with him,' she replied.

The director looked around and saw no one wearing a hat. He looked at the crew member so he could enlighten him.

'She was sitting alone in one corner when I spotted her. There was nobody there, sir,' the crew member said.

'See, beta, you are my responsibility when on the film set. Don't play pranks, please. I've crossed that age.' He gave her a candy and asked her to join the other children so they could start shooting.

All of a sudden, the girl started shaking, as if she was having a fit. Then, as if some unknown force had pushed her hard, she fell on the ground, rolled over and began babbling in an unknown language. Her arms were behind her, like someone was holding them together. The entire crew fled. Her distressed father and the director had no idea what to do. Somehow they managed to put her in a car and her father drove her away from the place. Unsure what should be the next step, he made calls to various people in his family. It certainly wasn't any medical condition—he knew that much. Strangely, his daughter was perfectly normal a few minutes after they'd left Mukesh Mills. And she had no memory of what had happened to her.

'Let's find out the truth behind it!' Gaurav said and greeted the Zee News crew who had just reached. They decided to have some tea and snacks at a nearby stall before entering the premises. While at it, they could plan a few things as well. When they were ready, the night guard let them in and asked them to stick together, but they knew that wouldn't be possible. The place was large and they would have to split up to cover the entire area. Gaurav and Siddharth formed one team along with Nikhil Dubey, the news reporter, while his two co-workers headed off with Robb.

9.53 p.m.
An hour passed, and there had been no activity so far. The news reporter, the most impatient among them, kept asking Gaurav if he had found anything. He needed his TRPs, after all; both time and effort were being invested in this case.

'No. Nothing so far—I can't lie,' Gaurav told him patiently. He himself was curious to find out more, but calmness was one of the veteran's virtues.

They were now at one end of Mukesh Mills; it had been a long walk. Dubey, a heavy man who had had a tiring day at work, suggested they sit for some time. There were no lights around at all. All they had were their flashlights to find their way. Which is why Siddharth found it a little strange to see a torch being flashed at the opposite end from where they sat.

'Who is there?' he called out, but realised his voice was probably not loud enough to reach the person. 'Please say something …' he shouted louder this time, waving his torch so it would catch the person's eye. 'Could it be another night guard sleeping inside?' he asked Gaurav. They knew Robb and the TV crew were in a different part of the mills.

'No, Siddharth. Let's go closer. Dubey-ji, you stay seated.' Gaurav switched on the EVP and asked Siddharth to start shooting.

They began walking towards the light and the EMF started spiking, moving higher as they got closer.

'Told you it's not!' Gaurav grinned with excitement as the activity had begun.

Siddharth began to capture everything on video and took pictures as well. It was dark and all they could see was someone holding a torch and seated. It looked like the person was wearing a dark-coloured shawl.

'Who are you?' Gaurav asked as they got very close.

The torch fell to the ground and there was nobody there.

Suddenly, the temperature dropped, which indicated a presence around them.

'We are here to communicate with you,' Gaurav said.

'Is it?' Dubey's voice came from right behind them, but it was a little different, a little … evil.

Gaurav and Siddharth turned around to see Dubey staring at them; it was as if the air around him was devoid of oxygen—there was a tightness in his throat and he struggled to breathe.

'What happened?' Gaurav hugged Dubey so he would feel better. Gaurav knew that these strange experiences were normal when it came to paranormal investigation, and it was important for the one who leads to be the strongest among them.

As Dubey calmed down, Siddharth told Gaurav, 'This place is the creepiest I have been to so far!'

11.21 p.m.

Robb and his two partners for the night were at the opposite end of where the other three were exploring, when they heard some noises—footsteps accompanied by growls.

'Could it be that there are animals in here?' Robb asked, though he knew the answer. The other two shook their heads, their expressions showing how petrified they were. Whatever made them agree to accompany Dubey, it wasn't worth their lives.

'Shhh, just stay quiet. Okay?' Robb consoled them and switched on his EVP.

'Anyone here?' he asked, and waited for a minute.

'Let's listen.' He then played the EVP recorder and heard that he had got what he was sure of. There was an audio anomaly after his question. Not clear at all, but he knew Siddharth could help him analyse it after the investigation.

'It wants to communicate!' Robb's eyes lit up. He looking around and said, 'Give us a sign that you are here, please.'

There was gust of cold wind the next moment, and it wasn't natural. The weather had been dry since morning, and it was hardly chilly.

'Good. Good. If you are male, give me two beeps on my EMF. If you are female, one!'

One beep.

'Did you die because of the fire here in 1982? One beep if yes, please.'

No answer.

'Er … what else could be the reason? Suicide?'

No answer.

'Murder?'

Beep!

'So, murders have taken place here too.' He looked at the two men so that they could take note while they shot on their video camera.

'Are you happy that we are talking to you? One beep, if yes.'

Beep!

1.05 a.m.

After exploring Mukesh Mills, they all met up at the same spot where they had split. That had been the plan.

'Sid, I'll need your help for audio anomalies. Got a couple of them,' Robb said as they gathered. Then they realised that someone was missing. Dubey wasn't there.

'He was with us just a few seconds ago.' Gaurav walked back a few steps to look around. He was nowhere to be seen!

'What is going on?' Dubey's co-workers were obviously a little scared, but did not panic because of the experts they were with.

'Let's search for him before it's too late.' Everyone with Gaurav during an investigation was his responsibility. So he knew, so he felt.

Just then there was a thunderstorm and it began raining heavily.

'Rain? In December?' Siddharth was baffled and so were the others.

'Maybe it's because this place is near the sea?' Robb suggested.

'Even then! It never rains during this time.' Siddharth had never seen this happen in all his years in Mumbai so far.

Calling out for Dubey, they started walking back from where they had come. This time they stayed together wherever they went.

Suddenly—'All good?' Dubey asked from behind.

'Where ... where were you?' Siddharth asked and breathed a sigh of relief at the same time; he had been worried about the reporter.

'But ... I was right here with you. What ... what happened?'

'Guys, we should leave. Too many bad things have happened here. The spirits are not at rest and are not really interested in communicating, apart from a few of them. We have the findings we require,' Gaurav said.

When they were at the gate, the watchman too commented on the rain and how unusual it was for that time of year.

Later, Siddharth analysed Robb's audio recording. He could hear a gruff voice, but could not make out what was being said. He also confirmed that the anomaly happened specifically when Robb was communicating with whatever was present there, and at no other time.

Mukesh Mills remains one of the most haunted places in the country and has been closed for many years now, no longer opened even for film shoots. The IPS is the only professional paranormal team that has been able to investigate it.

'You guys did so much, really. You know, we were talking about how Gaurav ran IPS without making much money out of the activities. I'm curious—how did he manage the show so well?' I asked. It's something that I had been wondering about.

'Sponsorships helped at times, but mostly we didn't even break even.'

April 2016
It had been a little over two months since Gaurav was married and he had been having a really difficult time balancing his professional duties and personal life. Earlier, even though his parents weren't happy about his profession, it hadn't affected things much. His father was largely worried about his son not earning money, and his mother was concerned about Gaurav's safety. He was from a well-off family, and money wasn't such a problem, but Gaurav never used it or even his father's contacts to run IPS. It was completely his baby, and while the growth had been immense, it wasn't so in monetary terms. Media coverage helped him and the team remain in the limelight, and some sponsors did show interest, but it was not enough to run the operations—office, team salaries, travel expenses, equipment.

It was difficult to figure out what Gaurav was really going through as well, since he always had a calm demeanour. Siddharth and Meghna could not recall ever seeing him lose his cool. Raj, who had spent more time with him, had seen him sad, but never angry. Not even on the day Gaurav and his wife had the big quarrel in Lansdowne. The least Gaurav could expect from his dear ones was some mental support. Of course, perhaps from their perspective, they might have been upset that he was so busy and couldn't take out much time for them. It was during this period that Meghna had a premonition, a terrible one, that would come true a few months later.

She had stayed back late in office that evening due to some pending work and had taken the last local from Bandra to Malad. The train was near-empty, a rarity in the city, but it was post peak hours and she was the only one in the ladies compartment. She plugged in her earphones and began listening to music. It had been a hectic week and she was all set to unwind over the weekend.

I'll bake a cake for Mom, watch a nice feel-good movie for a change and spend quality time at home, she thought. She looked out of the window, feeling the breeze on her face.

'Meghna …'

It was Gaurav's voice.

She turned and gaped. Was she hallucinating? But there he was! He was seated in one corner of the compartment.

'Gaurav …?'

He sat still, silent, looking at Meghna.

'Meghna …' His lips did not move, but the voice came from him. The already dim lights in the train flickered rapidly and went off in the next few seconds. He wasn't there anymore. The train stopped as well.

'Which ... which station?' she mumbled to herself as she walked up to the entrance to check. She looked out—it was none of the stations that came between Bandra and Malad—Khar Road, Santacruz, Vile Parle, Andheri, Jogeshwari, Goregaon. None of them. She knew what those stations looked like. Any daily commuter does. Moreover, this station was deserted. There wasn't anyone to be seen; neither were the shops open. It had now been close to a minute since the train had stopped. Why would the driver not start? Why would the train not move?

Small beads of sweat formed on Meghna's forehead.

'Which station?' she screamed at the top of her voice. It felt like she was in *the other world*. This wasn't a nightmare. She bit her tongue to check if she was dreaming. No—she could feel the pain.

The other world—the world of the dead, spirits, demons—a world that runs parallel to ours, but one where living beings don't dwell; more of a phase after death where people with emotional baggage are stuck, somewhere between the physical world and the light of salvation. But how come she was here without any astral projection—an out-of-body experience wherein one's soul leaves the body and travels there in the form of an astral body, perhaps consciously observing it from a detached perspective, like a soul?

Meghna decided to get down at the station and find her way out to the living physical world. She put a foot down on the platform when ...

'*Agla station, Andheri* (Next station, Andheri).' The lights came on, the small fans began running and the train started moving.

Meghna heaved a sigh of relief and sat down with a thud, thanking God that it was over—whatever it was.

'Meghna ...' Gaurav whispered again in her left ear. He was sitting there, beside her, looking at her without blinking his eyes. There was a deep black mark on his neck.

Meghna felt short of breath. The vision needed interpretation. She felt sure something terrible was going to happen ...

TWELVE

KULDHARA

When there is so little in the world to prove that ghosts exist, why should we be afraid of them? A person will remain the same even after physical death. Spirits and ghosts are not magical creatures that can play with someone's destiny and force someone beyond the physical limits.

— GAURAV TIWARI

October 2010

It had been a year since Gaurav had returned to India and established the IPS, which, in turn, formed the GRIP team to investigate paranormal activities. But it wasn't easy. The team wasn't taken seriously by most people, as paranormal research and investigation was something new to the country. Despite the odds, the IPS continued its work, researching the paranormal, educating people and doing shows on paranormal investigation for Indian news channels. The show MTV *Girls Night Out* happened during this time, when IPS was still in its nascent stage but beginning to gain momentum.

Hosted by VJ Rannvijay, in the show, three girls would be taken to a haunted location and left all alone for an entire night to brave the unknown. After assessing their performances, one would be selected and given the prize of five lakh rupees. With no crew, no phones and no connection with the outside world, these girls were in for one horrifying ride to be covered in real time, all alone! This hair-raising show took the help of Gaurav Tiwari and his GRIP partner then, Akanksha Kaushik. The two would first carry out investigations in the chosen location with modern equipment like K-II meters, EMF readers, infrared thermometers, night vision HD cameras and various software. The show was shot with the most modern equipment and lighting to give the best visual and sound effects.

Gaurav went to Kuldhara several times, but there were two visits in particular that he found really productive, one of which was for this show. Rannvijay, Gaurav, Akanksha, a few crew members and the three girls—Rubina, Nafisa and Tara—had reached Jaisalmer a day before the shooting would begin.

Kuldhara is less than an hour's drive from Jaisalmer. Established in the thirteenth century, this abandoned village in Rajasthan is among the most haunted places in the country. No one knows for sure why it was abandoned. Some say there was dwindling water supply during the nineteenth century; some attribute it to the believed persecution by a minister, Salim Singh, and there are others who believe that there was an earthquake. There is another theory that is related to Salim Singh too. In an era of powerful kings and ministers, about two hundred years ago, Kuldhara was home to the Paliwal Brahmins. It was during this time that Salim Singh, the diwan of Jaisalmer, known for his debauchery and unscrupulous tax-collecting methods, set his eyes on the beautiful daughter of the village chief. The diwan was absolutely hell-bent on having the girl, and he told the villagers that if they came in his way, he would levy huge taxes on them.

Fearing the wrath of the diwan, the residents of the entire village fled one dark night, leaving behind their homes and other belongings. No one saw the thousand-odd members of the village leave. For generations now, no one knows where the Paliwals resettled. But it is believed that they cursed the town when they left—that no one would ever be able to settle down in Kuldhara again. And the village remains barren and uninhabited till this day.

The team reached Kuldhara at around 6.45 p.m. after a late but sumptuous lunch. The drive from Jaisalmer itself had been fun. It was a dusty road that led to the haunted location; there was little sign of human existence, and vegetation was minimal too. There were only a few stray goats here and there, trying to find some fodder. They reached the remains of the village where an uncanny silence prevailed all around them. Rannvijay got down first to check out the surroundings.

'Damn, man. It's like a scene out of those old Ramsay horror movies! This place is creepy.' He stretched his arms and legs. It had been a short but bumpy ride, and the night would be tiring, perhaps frightening too!

And it was.

This incident happened with Rubina. It remained one of Gaurav's most memorable experiences, and he often talked about it in his interviews.

Rubina Aneja, born and brought up in Delhi, was an aspiring model and was preparing for this along with going to college. She was thoroughly excited to be a part of MTV *Girls Night Out* for two reasons—the visibility she would get through the hot new show on one of the channels with maximum TRP and the money, which she planned to use for a professional photo shoot. She would then complete her graduation and leave for Mumbai to try her luck. Of course, a few contacts and her stint with the show would help. She was not much of a believer in anything supernatural, until ...

10.45 p.m.
While Rannvijay, Gaurav, Akanksha and two crew members operated out of the car outside, the girls had gone into the ghost village. Apart from them, there was an old man, nearing his eighties, who had been guarding the gates for almost forty years; he lived in a nearby village with his son.

It was a full moon night and there was a strange breeze that was discomforting and saddening. Moonlight shone over the hard soil that stretched in every direction until the land rose to low hillocks. Between the derelict dwellings that had lost more than the people who lived there once, the wind was channelled to a low howl. When the sun dipped and moonlight was the only illumination for miles around, the phantoms and spectres rose from the ground or else stepped from the creaking walls. On the rare occasion that the living walked the dusty streets, the ghosts mostly remained invisible, but on full moon nights the rules were different. This was that kind of a night …

The girls went their separate ways, and in the midst of the ruins, Rubina observed that a temple and a few houses were being renovated. The Archaeological Survey of India had recently begun maintaining it as a heritage site, and the Rajasthan government was then on the verge of developing it as a tourist spot. The workers would come in the morning and leave by afternoon, as nobody was allowed in Kuldhara after sunset.

Rubina sat in a corner of an old house near the temple, waiting for the night to get over so that she could walk out with the prize and begin a new life, a life she had dreamt of ever since she had seen Sushmita Sen winning Miss Universe in 1994 on television.

'It's not about beauty, Mom. It's about brains too! Also, think about the kind of money and fame our family will get if I win,' she told her mother time and again to convince her. Born in a middle-class Delhi family in Karol Bagh, it wasn't easy for her to follow her dreams.

A few CCTV cameras were placed in the corner and other parts of the house. Gaurav and his team had visited a few places first earlier that evening to determine three hotspots where they could place the girls for the night. The EMF meters spiking at a few of the areas helped in doing so. The two crew members had placed CCTV cameras there and then joined Gaurav, Rannvijay and Akanksha, who would be watching from near the main gate. The contestants had also been provided with night vision cameras, full-spectrum cameras and flashlights.

Gaurav was more interested in going in and investigating the village further, but the format of the show was such that he couldn't do so. It was then that he decided to go back to Kuldhara again, which he did, not once but several times.

'Abhishek should have joined us on this one too!' Rannvijay told Gaurav as he smoked.

'He isn't keeping too well. We are missing him too.' Gaurav looked at Akanksha, who nodded. Abhishek was also a GRIP member and had been a part of many of the episodes.

'You guys are doing a fabulous job, GT! Trust me when I say this—years later you will be remembered and your name will be synonymous with paranormal investigation. You, my friend, are writing history. Cheers to that!' Rannvijay patted Gaurav and hugged him. They had bonded very well during the show.

1.50 a.m.
All the three girls were holding on strong. No paranormal activity had been reported yet, and Gaurav was disappointed. When he, Rannvijay and Akanksha had visited the place earlier in the evening, the EMF meter had spiked in several places and he had felt this would be a significant breakthrough for IPS and GRIP.

Meanwhile, while Rubina may not have experienced anything yet, simply being there all by herself was blood-curdling. Added to this was the musty smell of the house that had been long abandoned: it filled her nose, and it seemed to remain with her every second. The doors and windows, dusty and old, looked as if they would crumble if someone touched them. Mould ate away at the walls and flooring, and cobwebs laced the corners and portraits of people who had once lived in the house. Nothing of interest was there in the room barring a trunk of old moth-eaten clothes. It was now that Rubina felt as if someone, or something, was watching her, waiting to drag her into the shadows.

'Rubina ...' It was the voice of one of the crew members. She didn't know him too well, but knew it was Danny's voice. It had come from outside the house.

'I thought this wasn't in the rules of the game!' Rubina answered.

'The show is over. Come out, let's leave,' Danny informed her.

'Just like that? Who wins?' Rubina stood up.

There was no answer.

'Danny?' No answer.

Rubina walked up to the door to check for him, but there was nobody. Could it be that he had informed her and left quickly? Perhaps he had gone to tell the other girls too. Rubina decided she should walk to the main gate as swiftly as possible without looking back.

'Someone tell me I won!' she mumbled to herself and crossed her fingers.

'You won!' she thought she heard someone whisper in her ear and laugh.

Just then, Rubina saw a dark figure slowly advancing as she walked hesitantly down the abandoned alley, impersonating every movement she made. A flicker of the torch and she momentarily lost sight of the figure; but then, to her horror, it rose out of the murky depths of a mud puddle again, breathing life into the cold cobblestone. The grim outline of a shadowy reflection possessed her and she wasn't herself the next moment …

The show had to be stopped when she couldn't be contacted. The last the team had seen her on CCTV was when she had left the house, calling Danny's name. But Danny had been with the crew near the main gate! It wasn't he who had spoken to her from outside the house. A few minutes later, they all began searching for Rubina in every nook and corner of Kuldhara. This was scary not just because of the supernatural occurrence, but also because she was the responsibility of the makers of MTV *Girls Night Out*. A search followed and continued till the wee hours of the morning till Rubina was found lying unconscious many kilometres away from Kuldhara. The show had to be called off and the case remained etched in the minds of everyone present there.

February 2014

By now, the IPS was a brand people believed in; it was synonymous with paranormal research and investigation in the country. The media coverage did help, but everyone also recognised the scientific and mostly undebatable approach they had towards unravelling the truth behind inexplicable happenings. Such was the traction of IPS that they didn't have to approach news channels anymore; rather, it was the other way round now. Zee News was one of the many channels that loved to cover their investigations in real time during this period. The IPS team had already visited Kuldhara with other news channels, including Aaj Tak in 2011, but this time would turn out to be the most productive.

Raj was a part of the team by now and a lot had changed in terms of their technical prowess after his joining. It also helped that he had become a very close friend of Gaurav's—the work he did was not restricted to the professional angle and his interest in the paranormal; he also wanted his best friend to always excel, along with the team. Raj went all out during each and every case, and he became very popular in the field due to the goodwill he built. In fact, there was a time when people were of the opinion that if there was any paranormal investigator after Gaurav Tiwari who was as much admired and sought-after, it was him. Needless to say, they made a terrific duo.

It was a chilly night in February when they reached Kuldhara with the Zee News team; the sort of cold winter that would freeze the blood of those who didn't take sufficient care to be warmly dressed. Their breath rose in visible puffs to join the darkened, clouded night sky. Almost rosy-cheeked, they stamped their feet to keep warm, pulling woollen caps over their reddened ears, tightening scarves over their blue-tinged lips. Their teeth chattered and the cold seeped into their gloves, numbing the fingers until, stiffened and frigid, they ceased to bend properly. The winter wind howled through the desolate ghost village as they walked inside with their equipment and cameras. This was a full moon night too, but a much colder one.

12.25 a.m.

The IPS team had set up several CCTV cameras in different parts of the village, and these were being monitored by Raj. It was only after midnight that an intelligent communication was determined with the entities, and this began with three of the cameras going blank and malfunctioning.

'This is not possible!' Raj told the Zee News reporter covering it with his three crew members.

Gaurav was in a different part of the village then, using his EVP and trying to communicate with the spirits. He would ask a question and then keep quiet, expecting to hear audio anomalies later, and he was bang on!

'What is the colour of my jacket?' he asked.

'Black.' The anomaly he heard was clear. They wanted to communicate.

'Tell me what happened here.' He smiled, satisfied that this would be a crucial finding. He had been to Kuldhara at least six times so far, and none of the visits had made him as happy as this one.

Meanwhile, Raj was determined to find out what was messing with the CCTV cameras.

'Hold on here till I come back!' he told the reporter as he sprinted towards one of the places where the camera had malfunctioned. He carried a night vision camera and EMF meter with him. He approached the hut that crouched in the shadows like a sleeping bear. This lumpy den of mud walls with a small opening in the front, barely large enough for a scrawny child to crawl through, was covered with torn branches and brown bracken.

'Raj ...' someone called out, and Raj looked back. It was a male voice. He could see someone there, a little distance away. The figure stood still, more like a shadow under the light of the full moon. He stood looking at Raj, as if wanting to tell him something.

'Who are you?' Raj turned the camera towards him, but it wouldn't work!

'What the ...' Raj banged one side of the camera. Battery problem?

But the figure was gone by then.

2.05 a.m.

Gaurav made his way to a dilapidated hut where he had detected some activity due to the spike in his K-II meter. He had his torchlight, but the darkness was so intense that the ray of light ended a few inches away from him. The rest of the room was pitch dark.

'I have kept a device here,' he said as he placed an EMF meter on the ground and walked away to sit down. Investigations were tiring yet fun, and there was a reason most were carried out at night. When asked why these were never done during the day, Gaurav would explain that paranormal activities are better traced when the environment is silent. Ghosts are around us even when it isn't dark. But why don't we get scared during the day? Simply because there is no darkness, and darkness leads to fear—fear of the unknown.

'If there is anyone here, please spike the meter thrice,' he said in his usual calm tone.

The very next second, it did spike ... thrice!

3.40 a.m.

The team had come out by then, exhausted, but their work was not done. They would now assemble in Gaurav's room in the hotel to review the findings. They knew Gaurav did not like to keep things pending even for a few hours. But something horrific was about to happen as they approached their cars. It was Raj who brought it to their notice, and they all saw it and took photos of it too. The hand print of a small child, possibly below five years of age, was on the rear glass of one of the cars.

'There are no people here, not within a radius of five kilometres at least.' Raj looked at Gaurav, who knew this.

'Monkeys?' the Zee News reporter asked.

'Not a chance! This is a desert area. Can't be monkeys,' Raj said.

'Click as many photographs as possible,' Gaurav instructed Raj as he drank some water.

'How was your experience this time, Gaurav?' the reporter wanted a quick news byte.

'Let's just say eventful! We can only conclude after the post-investigation work, but it seems that we got strong evidence. I can still say it is the most haunted place in India.' He smiled in his trademark style.

'Tourism has soared like anything in Kuldhara during the last few years, and it all began with your first visit here. What do you have to say?'

'See, that's not what I work for. It's nice to know it for sure. *Koi toh hamare kaam ka credit de raha hain* (At least someone is giving us credit for our work).' He laughed and asked the reporter if they could do this later. There wasn't anything concrete he could say now, not before the investigation was fully done.

Right then one of the car generators caught fire! Flickering and weaving, the fire flashed into existence in a wash of red and yellow sparks. A shrieking ray of melting gas propelled out of the flame's heat. The onlookers were shocked at first, then terrified—both emotions led them to be numb for a few seconds till a subtle shift in the wind brought noxious smoke and ash raining down onto their hair and into their eyes. With hands and clothing clamped to their mouths, it was chaos the next moment as they fled to the other car, hoping to all fit in. The message was loud and clear from the ghosts of Kuldhara. *Don't mess with us*. They were in no mood to be friendly with humans.

THIRTEEN

THE CASE WITH A HISTORY

Humans have a dual nature: a physical body and an ethereal aspect that contain the personality and consciousness. This ethereal aspect has been called the soul, spirit and 'higher self', among other things.

— GAURAV TIWARI

March 2016

Lata Mehta and her five-year-old son had just had a Skype call with her husband, Pravesh, who was based in Doha for work. He would travel on and off to Mumbai to visit his wife and son, but it had been almost a year now that he hadn't been able to do so due to excessive workload and job responsibilities. His parents lived in Kolkata, as did Lata's father, brothers and her elder brother's seven-year-old daughter. Pravesh's was a Gujarati family that was into the jewellery business, but he had decided long ago he wouldn't follow in his father's footsteps. So he had done his MBA from a reputed B-School and bagged a job with a prestigious MNC. It had been three years now that he had been working in Doha. He had decided against relocating his family there, as he didn't plan to be in Doha for long. In fact, he had already requested his reporting authority for a transfer back to Mumbai.

'Sleep well, beta.' Lata kissed her son's forehead and switched off the light. She lay down beside him to check Facebook updates on the phone till she dozed off to sleep, which she did only to be woken up at around 3 a.m.

'Maa ...' It was her son's voice. She rubbed her eyes as she opened them. She could see him faintly in the darkness standing next to her.

'All good? Why are you awake?' she asked him and switched on the table lamp. But there was nobody there.

'Maa...'someonewhispered,someonewhowassittingnext to her.

Lata looked beside her but her son wasn't there either! She jumped out of her bed and called out loudly for him.

'Samarth ... Samarth ...'

No answer. Just then, the light switches turned on, then off, on, then off again. At the same time, Lata heard footsteps coming from the drawing room. Someone was walking to and fro, from probably the kitchen area to the main door of the apartment, and it got louder with every second. Then there were tapping sounds on the window of the bedroom.

'Maa ...' the voice came again from near the window.

A paralysing fear spread through Lata's body like icy, liquid metal. She clenched her fists as she hesitantly took each step, noticing her legs were trembling. Fighting the impulse to whirl around and sprint away from the room, she walked forward, her mouth dry.

'Maa …' Samarth hugged his mother from behind. A shocked Lata looked back to see her son.

'Where … where were you?'

'Here itself, Maa. On the bed. Didn't you see me?' he wept as he hugged her tightly. The next moment, the knocking and footstep sounds were gone.

'It hurts, Maa,' Samarth cried as he showed her his arms and stomach. There were a series of fingerprints on her son's body!

'What's happening here!' Lata shrieked, feeling her son's pain. She immediately called her father and asked him to come with her younger brother to Mumbai and stay with them for a few days.

'I'll explain when you are here tomorrow,' she said and disconnected the call.

A week after this incident, Meghna was contacted through the IPS website by Lata. Meghna called Gaurav and explained the case to him and Gaurav asked her to go ahead and investigate it with Siddharth, Rith and Mohan.

'I'm not really in the right frame of mind, Meghna. Can you take this up? I'm sure you will exceed my expectations,' he told her, sounding a little low.

Siddharth was in Delhi then, but flew down the same day for the investigation.

The team reached the upscale apartment in the evening and were surprised to see an old man open the door. He introduced himself as Lata's father. Her brother greeted them with a smile and made a call on his mobile phone.

'Didi, they are here. Have a word,' he said and handed the phone to Meghna.

The IPS team learnt that Lata had been spending the last few days at a friend's place. Things had got even worse after her father and brother had come from Kolkata the very next morning post her call.

'We are staying at a hotel too, since yesterday. We just came for the investigation,' Lata's father informed the team.

'I suggested that Lata stay away from the house with the child. See, it seems like the entity is mostly troubling your grandson. But we weren't aware that you would be here,' Meghna said. She instructed the team to get the equipment ready and asked if there had been any more occurrences after Lata had contacted them.

'Yes. Yes,' her father nodded, his hands trembling in fear, as if being in the house was the last thing he wanted.

'But we will tell you once you are done with the investigation. We want to know your views first,' Lata's brother, Rajneesh, requested.

'It's better that we know before we begin. It's part of the protocol,' Siddharth said.

'Don't get us wrong, please. We aren't rigid. But like you need to tell the doctor your problems before he or she can treat you, it's important for us to know as well in order to analyse the situation better,' Mohan added.

So Rajneesh began talking. He said the creepiest incident had been when one of his friends had come over for dinner. It had been years since they'd met. Since it was late, they had asked him to spend the night in the apartment. Everything was fine till around 2 a.m., when he woke up to drink water and had to cross the hallway to enter the kitchen. As per the CCTV camera which they had installed a few days ago, the friend stood still for almost thirty minutes, mumbling something to himself. Lata happened to get up, and when she heard something, she woke her father and brother up, and they went to the hallway where the sound was coming from. There the friend stood, looking at them—his eyes were all white!

'Rana!' Rajneesh screamed, hoping it would work.

The next moment, the expression on his friend's face transformed quickly from blankness to confusion to panic. He had no clue what he was doing there, or why the others were looking at him with such fear, but he understood something very bad must have happened. He could sense it.

'There is something about the hallway,' Rajneesh told the IPS team. A day before this incident, he had heard things being thrown about in the washroom that was close to the hallway. When he had gone to check, he had witnessed someone walking about there, and it was no one from the family! He had been too scared to go to that washroom after that.

He then showed the IPS team the CCTV footage of the friend getting possessed.

'We can't conclude anything from this. It could be something to do with his mental condition as well, you see,' Rith said. Gaurav had trained the team well: *while approaching any case, look at it like a non-believer and see if there is a logical explanation behind any activity.*

'And what do you have to say about this?' Rajneesh showed them another video—in this there was a ball of light floating in one of the rooms.

'It is common for such things to happen with CCTV cameras, as the light from the infrared illuminator reflects dust particles and insects. Then you may get such visuals,' Meghna said.

'I was pushed to the floor by an unknown force two days ago, Meghna,' Rajneesh said. He started crying then. 'I've never been a believer in such things. But this place … this place is terrible. Do you not get any feeling?' he pleaded.

'I'm sorry, I didn't get your name yet.' Meghna realised they had been so caught up with the discussion, she had forgotten to ask his name.

'Rajneesh.'

'Okay. Rajneesh, we never arrive at any conclusion until we are sure. Guys, are we ready?'

Siddharth headed to the hallway to take some photographs. The dark and shadowy hallway was illuminated for a split second. The camera let out a small whirring sound. A small photo slid out. Siddharth retrieved the photo, waved it in the air for a minute and then looked at it. He gulped as he stared at the photo and then at what appeared before him—a murky shadow was leaping from the wall approximately five feet away. Siddharth felt uncomfortable and wanted to call out to his team members who were still near the front door. The presence in the house was evil, very evil.

Thump, thump, thump. Thump, thump.

Siddharth heard knocks come thrice at a time, and then twice. He swallowed.

'Um, hello?' he called out tentatively, taking a step towards the end of the hallway where the sound had come from.

Taking a deep breath, he approached the door. He raised his fist to knock, and in his subconscious he realised he was doing it all as if he was under some kind of spell. There was no answer. He tried again; no one answered. A shaky sigh escaped his parted lips.

'Anyone here?' he whispered.

Without warning, the shadow seemed to rise from behind him. Siddharth stood there frozen and stunned. He could feel some kind of a presence move towards him and darkness surrounded him like a mist. The presence and mist then disappeared, but Siddharth knew something was in that room, and that entity wasn't happy.

Siddharth shared his experience with the rest of the team and they split up to work separately. It was past midnight. By now, Meghna could confirm to the family that the apartment was indeed haunted. She was in the bedroom with her full spectrum camera and EVP recorder …

'Show yourself,' she said as she looked around and took as many photographs as she could. A ball of light manifested in front of her eyes the next second, floated in the air and then disappeared. Before she could do anything, a jolt shook her up—more like that of static electricity. Abruptly, a chill rose up her spine, making her shiver. Something was there with her in the room and she could feel it, sense it. Sounds of hushed whispering seemed to be erupting and spilling from the peeling wallpaper. This couldn't be happening. Or was it? Was she actually hearing and seeing things?

This isn't real, she told herself, but the signs were too evident. It felt nothing but real and absolute to her.

A breath, hoarse and faint, echoed around her, coming from the south of the room. Meghna slowly turned her head and the whispering stopped. The air chilled to ice and her laboured breathing became the only sound ...

Then she saw it! It was hanging from the ceiling, crawling ever so slowly towards her, dark and brooding.

Creak. Crrk. Creak. Crrk. Crreakk.

Siddharth was in the other bedroom doing his own investigation at the same time. Like Meghna was an expert in taking photographs, he excelled in analysing audio anomalies, and he was using his EVP recorder now.

'Do you have anything to do with the child in this house?' he asked, coming directly to the point. Most of the incidents that had transpired had some relation to the child. It was he who was getting the most tormented too. The signs were clear.

'*Haan* (Yes).' It sounded like whatever was there had given an intelligent response to the question being asked. 'Intelligent' entities are the ones that give a direct response to the questions being asked, and this was one.

Siddharth saw the shadow again, this time seeping up through the joints of the door and snaking out from dark corners and crevices. The blackness formed from some primeval hatred and the collective despair of all that was taken from it when alive. It kept on growing, growing till

Siddharth couldn't see the cupboard he was standing close to; he couldn't see the bed or any object in the room. He did think for a minute that it could be his eyes adjusting to the darkness or simply fatigue, but the voice anomaly and, now, the EMF meter spiking at an all-time high confirmed the presence of an entity there.

But it was Rith who determined the crux of the case. Like the other team members, he was also sure that the entity had something to do with the child. So he made Lata's father communicate with the entity while he observed for a while.

'Do we know you?' the father asked.

Beep.

'Are you from the family?'

Beep.

'What's your name?' Rith asked.

There was an answer. Rith looked at the father and his son, who were completely shaken. There was something they had been hiding. Rith continued the conversation after this, which led them to finding out a lot more. After this, Meghna got the remaining team together so they could leave and discuss Plan B. They had to think of different questions to ask the entity so there was proper closure.

'Who is Geetanjali?' Rith asked Lata the next day, when the team met her at a café.

'Geetanjali? My sister-in-law …' Lata's lips quivered as she began joining the dots.

'What happened to her, Lata?' Meghna asked. The haunting was visceral and had affected them. This was no mere entity trying to communicate. It had a deeper purpose.

Tears rolled down Lata's cheeks as she recalled her simple, kind and lovely sister-in-law who had been married to her elder brother, Pushpendra. It had been an arranged marriage, and they had both been very young at the time. The families had met through a mutual contact; a few things had been discussed with respect to their businesses, fewer things about the future of the youngsters. It was basically a deal in which the girl's parents were happy that they had got a good family for their daughter, and the son's parents had thought they would be able to pay off some debts. Yes, dowry was negotiated. But Geetanjali's parents finally couldn't arrange the amount. So, her in-laws had begun ill-treating Geetanjali. The husband had been no better. Under terrible pressure due to a failed business and losses mounting up, he did the same. Geetanjali stuck to the marriage; she thought a child would change things. They had a daughter, but things just got worse. Pushpendra would sometimes even beat her in front of the little one, taking out all his frustrations at the end of the day on a woman who hadn't been a good monetary proposition for him. Geetanjali couldn't take it after a point. She finally gave up and told her parents that she would be filing for a divorce and returning home.

'No, you will not. We will arrange for the money in parts,' her father had told her.

'What after that? They will ask for more. Greed never ends,' she had told him. By then, she had realised it was futile trying to adjust with a family that understood only money.

'Things are very bad here for me, Ma,' she had added.

'You are a woman. You have to adjust,' her mother had said and disconnected the call.

That day, Geetanjali had felt she had lost. She had ended her life, leaving behind a note that wasn't too clear about the reasons. Maybe she hadn't wanted any action taken against the family and wanted them to look after her daughter. Perhaps she had thought her daughter would grow up in a better environment after her mother's death.

Pushpendra was tried in court for abetment of suicide and acquitted due to lack of evidence. It was during this time, after Geetanjali's death by suicide, that the family had sent the daughter to live with Lata and her husband for almost two years. Lata hated her parents and Pushpendra for what they had done, but had kept quiet as she felt it was not her business. She had made sure that she and her husband took very good care of Geetanjali's daughter, Amishi, who was just one then.

Lata's mother had come to stay with them for a month at one point. One day, she fell from the balcony and died. The family had thought she slipped, however, the maid told the police that she had seen her jump, and that it was a case of suicide. A curse seemed to have fallen upon the family! But there had been no supernatural occurrences till now.

'Where is Amishi now?' Meghna asked.

'In our Kolkata home with my elder brother. When Pravesh and I had a son, my brother asked us to send her back.'

'There you are!' Meghna's eyes lit up as she figured out the reason for the haunting.

'I'm sorry?'

'Geetanjali wants you to raise Amishi. This is what she wants to communicate to you. Don't you get it?'

'But Meghna …'

'Your elder brother isn't taking care of his daughter properly, Lata. We suggest you to take up this responsibility, and Geetanjali's spirit won't harm you and your son,' Meghna counselled.

I left the office for some fresh air before we began to talk about other cases. The one they had just told me about was certainly a disturbing one, and I was eager to hear about the others.

It had stopped raining a while ago, but as per the weather forecast, there was more to come. The stars in the sky were non-existent; grey clouds hovered above like an armed patrol, hiding the full moon behind them. The moon fought to shine its light on earth, but the clouds stretched over the sky, giving it a hazy, ominous feel.

I walked back in and settled down, ready to hear about another investigation.

FOURTEEN

BOGGO ROAD GAOL INVESTIGATION WITH HAUNTING: AUSTRALIA TEAM

I believe for everything to manifest in reality, it has to first exist in our minds. Today, we can very well say that ghosts (in most cases) are nothing but products of our imaginations. It also depends on who you ask. For most people, ghosts are scary, ugly, spooky creatures who only mean to harm humanity.

– GAURAV TIWARI

Located in Brisbane in Queensland, Australia, Boggo Road Gaol was the main jail in the state from the 1880s to 1980s. Its stark red brick walls and imposing guard tower on Annerley Road have become iconic for all the wrong reasons over the many years.

It was opened in 1883 as the Brisbane Gaol. Used mainly as a holding prison for those serving short sentences or on remand, its initial infamy came from it being a place where executions took place. Boggo Road was where some of the nation's most infamous criminals lived and died, including the Whiskey Au Go Go bombers James Richard Finch and John Andrew Stuart; 'Slim' Halliday, the 'Houdini of Boggo Road'; Florence MacDonald, charged with the murder of her daughter, and Ernest Austin, a child-killer who was to be the last man of forty-two prisoners executed in the state of Queensland. It is said that Austin, who was hanged for the brutal murder of eleven-year-old Ivy Mitchell in 1913, is one of the ghosts who has been seen passing through walls in the jail. As per reports, he had laughed hysterically just before his death.

30 January 2015

Gaurav joined Allen, Robb, Rayleen and Mama Owl Paranormal (an investigation team that accompanied them for a night) for this case. Ian and Ray couldn't make it due to other commitments, but did give their inputs on it.

It was a hot and humid summer day. The sky blazed blue and the sun was a celebration of yellow, free and bright. The trees rose to the occasion, donning their best verdant hues, and everywhere there were flowers, a scattered rainbow. 'Too bad we don't have this kind of summer back in Delhi. It's just hot and humid, not colourful really,' Gaurav said with a laugh. He always tried to lighten the mood for himself and others before an investigation, as he felt the best output was derived when people had fun at work.

A few days ago ...

The jail, always known for its poor conditions and rioting, became the focus of national media scrutiny again in the 1980s after hunger strikes and protests over the poor conditions in which No. 2 Division inmates were being kept. That division was shut in 1989, and the entire prison complex closed in 2002 with the Brisbane Women's Correctional Centre ceasing operations. In December 2012, the gaol was reopened for tourists, with guided tours being offered.

Jimmy was a janitor who had been working at the gaol for a few weeks. This incident happened to him in broad daylight.

Daily tours are conducted in Boggo Road Gaol for tourists interested in its history and other aspects; there is one for ghosts and gallows too. That day was no different. A few groups were let into the jail and were being shown around the place by their guides while Jimmy was doing his routine work in the hallways of the jail—dark floors and white walls, not a handprint or a scuff mark anywhere. The doors were a glossy black, numbered with silver digits that matched the globe-shaped handles.

Footsteps echoed sharply in the deserted hallway Jimmy was cleaning.

'Excuse me, mister. Could you help me with the way here? I seem to be lost.' Jimmy saw a man walk up to him, seemingly in a hurry.

Jimmy could observe him better once he was a little nearer. His curls were midnight black and his eyes were dark brown, framed by graceful brows. His skin was tanned. He had prominent cheekbones, a well-defined chin and nose, and sported a thin fuzzy beard.

'Tour?' Jimmy asked.

'Yes. Yes. That's right.'

'Come, I'll show you the way.'

The first day Jimmy had come to Boggo Road Gaol, he was trained by his supervisor to be courteous and helpful to tourists. It was because of them that the heritage site could be maintained well.

'So, where are you from, sir?' Jimmy tried to strike up a conversation with the man. There was a guest book at the reception where tourists were asked to provide their remarks about the place and people; perhaps this man would mention the janitor's willingness to help.

'Victoria. You new here?' the man asked, walking a little behind Jimmy.

'Ye-yes. How did you know that?' Jimmy had tried to sound like an expert, but perhaps he looked too young to be a veteran of the place. That could be the reason.

'Just.' He was a man of few words, it seemed.

Once they arrived near the main gate, Jimmy turned around to tell the man that he could wait there till the group arrived. 'But you could have just called them—' he began to say as he turned, but stopped short. There was nobody there.

'Where did that man go?' he asked the gatekeeper who was there when they walked up to the reception at the main gate.

'What man? You came here alone,' the gatekeeper said.

'No way! There was this tourist from Victoria. Show me the guest list for today,' he said.

'Jimmy ... Jimmy ... hang on, boy! You must have encountered the spirit of Ernest Austin, the child killer. Many others have seen him here. He sometimes takes the form of other people too. You never know. And yes, he was from Victoria.'

Gaurav had two pieces of equipment in mind for this case: the EVP recorder for voice anomalies and the Echovox, which he rarely used. It is an audio sensory device too, but with a difference. A piece of software that can run on a smartphone or a PC tablet, it can be discreetly used at a location. EVP, or electronic voice phenomena, is the known phenomena wherein voices for which there is no discernible natural source are captured on electronic devices. It has long been suggested that such audible captures, which may be single words or phrases, are the result of non-physical communication, or, in other words, spirits leaving a message. The Echovox system is an advanced technology in which a further step is taken along this path of communication. It's a real-time system, unlike digital Dictaphone sessions, where we have the ability to hear the feedback live or with a slight delay. This is enhanced with the ability to record all sessions for later analysis. It incorporates a natural loop echo system, that, when added to the sound bank's phonetics, creates a random chaotic condition under sound that is open to spirits' communication through system manipulation. In other words, creating order out of chaos and pinpointing coherence. The application has a sound bank which consists of vowels and consonants in male and female voices. Researchers believe the energies have the ability to manipulate these random sounds to form a word that serves as a medium of instant communication.

The team decided to stay together while examining the cells of the prison, except for one session where they split up.

11.33 p.m.
'We just want to know what happened here. We are here to communicate,' Gaurav said, setting up the Echovox. He and Rayleen were together during this session.

'What's your name?' Gaurav asked.

There was no answer.

'Can you hear me? All I want you to do is try hard and answer us on this machine.'

He would never give up. That wasn't Gaurav's style!

'*Put … Ellen … on …*' the Echovox buzzed.

'You know my name? It's Gaurav Tiwari.' He smiled and walked to one corner of the cell.

'Hmm, is there anyone you don't like in this team?'

'*Such a prick!*' Someone laughed.

'Is there anyone with you who doesn't want you to communicate with us?'

Gaurav sensed that there was more than one entity present at the time.

'*Fuck off!*' the one who wasn't interested in communicating said. '*Get out of here!*' it said, in fury.

'Did you die here?' Gaurav was focused on continuing the communication with the spirit who was interested.

But he didn't get an answer to this. It might have been because there were many entities there—very few interested in talking, others irate, some not synchronised with what was going on.

A few of the sounds that came after this seemed to be, *'My cell'*, *'suffering'* and *'expect'*.

'Where are you right now?' he asked.

'Cell 2.'

'Human being,' an entity said, probably observing them.

'Are you in pain?'

'No. We are dead.'

'Help us, Gaurav,' a voice said.

'Some women killed them!'

'Is there someone stopping you from communicating with us?'

'Fuck off.' Laughter.

'You have permission to use my energy to manifest yourselves,' Gaurav said.

'Bill.'

'I'm still not convinced that you exist,' Gaurav taunted, expecting some reaction. 'You have done nothing to convince me!' he said.

Then something passed through them! It felt like passing through an icy shower, like touching arctic air, like bathing in a tub full of ice cubes, like having every warm feeling and thought sucked out of you. There it was— someone was there! Gaurav saw the apparition of a man pass through the walls of the cells. It started with a slight shimmer, as if the air in front of him was being warped and twisted. Then, in a flash of pale, silvery light, a man appeared before him. He was dressed in old-fashioned clothes—a crisp white button-up, shirt sleeves rolled up to the elbows and a plain black vest with matching pants. Before he disappeared, Gaurav realised that it was the man from the painting in the hallway they had seen while entering the place.

Ernest Austin, the child killer. Executed on 22 September 1913. This was what Gaurav had read.

He had been only twenty-three and had raped and murdered an eleven-year-old girl named Ivy Mitchell. Twenty-three, but he looked much older—there was no innocence in the face; he had been a vicious criminal who was not one bit sorry about the heinous crime he had committed.

But it was the name Ellen that had been heard through the Echovox system. Ellen Thompson, the only woman to be hanged under Queensland law in 1887. She had been found guilty for the murder of her husband William Thompson by way of shooting him in the head. It seemed as if her spirit was keen on communicating with Gaurav, from what they had heard during the session. Gaurav wanted to know more about her once they were out of there, and so he went straight to the room where records were kept.

He learnt from the caretaker that Ellen's husband had been twenty-four years older than her and was violently abusive towards her. After his death, Ellen was charged for his murder. She proclaimed her innocence, but she and her lover John Harrison were convicted. They were hanged in Boggo Road jail and buried in the South Brisbane cemetery. On the day of his execution, the caretaker said, John Harrison had confessed that he had shot and killed William Thomson alone, in self-defence, but the admission was too late.

'Thanks, Mr …?' Gaurav looked at his uniform, but there was no badge.

'Frank. Frank Taylor.' He grinned.

'Thanks, Mr Taylor.' Gaurav took a snapshot of the page from the file and handed it back to him.

'A few spirits here are in a lot of pain, Robb. One of them is Ellen Thompson's for sure,' Gaurav told Robb. They were back in their hotel room, preparing to analyse the evidence as they sipped their morning tea at 4 a.m., happy about yet another successful investigation carried out.

I asked a question that had been revolving in my mind for a few days now. It was something I'd heard and read about on various news outlets. Most reports had either one of these two opinions: the paranormal investigator had died by suicide due to personal reasons, or an evil entity had been troubling him since the time he had visited a haunted house in Janakpuri. As per these news articles, on which IPS refuses to comment as they don't agree with the conjecture, Gaurav had been investigating the possession of a girl in a house in Janakpuri. He had gone there thrice in the last ten days before his death. According to family members, he had been there a few hours before his death too.

'Like I told you earlier, I was in the office that night. Gaurav spent some time with me before leaving for his home. Yes, I did feel something had been worrying him for the last couple of days, but it couldn't be an evil spirit. And we don't know anything about him visiting a haunted house in Janakpuri,' Siddharth said.

'Gaurav believed spirits exist because they are in pain. There is no real intent to cause any harm. We at IPS continue to live out his vision and thoughts. One needs to be empathetic towards ghosts, like you call them,' Meghna remarked.

'So, you mean to say there are no evil spirits?' I asked, my tone a little sarcastic.

'There are. But why would they harm you if you didn't do anything? Think.' Meghna smiled, understanding that I may not be on the same page as them.

'And all that we have seen and read while growing up ...'

'We have seen exaggerations on screen. We grow up to believe what people have fed us and our thoughts. What we are telling you here is the truth and nothing but the truth.'

'Okay, okay. I'm not arguing,' I said, flinging my hands up in the air. I asked them to continue.

'We are ruling out the possibility of him being affected by the work he did,' Meghna said.

Dr Jitender Nagpal, a mental health expert, when interviewed by *The Times of India,* had said the following regarding Gaurav's death: 'It is not improbable for paranormal investigators to be affected by their work. Any person dealing with cases of extra-sensory or surrealistic nature are prone to develop anxiety or depression. Such a person has to constantly deal with two worlds, which may lead to a level of alienation even from the loved ones. In turn, this could lead to aggression.'

While the police had not commented on whether his work with the paranormal had any connection with his death, they did not deny the possibility. Their line of investigation was aimed at establishing whether his constant encounters with unexplained phenomena could have led to depression or behavioural disturbances. The cops felt that this aspect of his life could be crucial in understanding why an overtly happy thirty-two-year-old would commit suicide.

Gaurav's wife, Arya, did mention that her husband had told her that some negative force had been pulling him inexorably in the last few days. Or perhaps it was that he was under tremendous psychological stress for reasons mostly unknown, unless you joined the dots.

FIFTEEN

KHABA FORT / JAISALMER FORT

Near-death experiences and shared-death experiences are a few things that really prove that physical death is not the end of our consciousness. The term human spirits is devoted to the consciousness of people who once lived as human beings. However, inhuman spirits are entities who never walked the earth as human beings.

— GAURAV TIWARI

February 2014

Gaurav Tiwari, his team and Zee News had covered Kuldhara a night ago and taken a day off—not to unwind, but for post-investigation work. Since they were in Jaisalmer, they decided they would explore other haunted places there too.

Khaba Fort is a small fort standing over a ruined settlement. Partly reconstructed by the Archaeological Survey of India, the site still has an unsettling, desolate vibe.

Once filled with people, it is now mostly home to peacocks and other birds. Though there is a village nearby, and there is even a museum with a collection of fossils on display, you can't shake off the feeling of an eerie silence that tends to build up around you—either because it is a remote location or there is something more sinister lurking there.

Located in the giant Thar desert, the ruined Khaba Fort was once the epicentre of Kuldhara village. The village of Khaba was home to the Paliwal Brahmins from the late thirteenth century, just like Kuldhara was. Around eighty to ninety families used to live in the village. Then, as with Kuldhara, supposedly one night in 1825, all the villagers left the place—no one knows why. Localites will tell you that it might have been because an earthquake shook the village or that there was a dwindling water supply. There are also stories of a king forcing a Brahmin girl to marry him, after which things went haywire.

The team decided to investigate the fort at night and managed to get permission for this. However, as soon as they reached the location the next day, they saw a few groups of locals blocking the entry; they looked as if they were willing to use force to stop them. They shouted that the team was spreading superstition by researching about ghosts in their town. Gaurav and team IPS had to wait till the next night to get the matter sorted by the local administration.

This happened while they were waiting for the situation to get resolved.

Gaurav and Raj were at the restaurant in the hotel for a buffet breakfast when they met Nishant Bhadoria, a businessman who introduced himself as a big fan.

'I love the work you are doing, sir!' He couldn't control his excitement on meeting him. 'Can I take a picture, please?' he asked.

Gaurav was always a little shy when he was complimented by strangers, but was happy that people respected what he did.

Once, when he was asked by *Nat Geo Traveller* what people back in India thought about him and his work, he had said, 'Humanity is full of diverse belief systems. Almost every client I meet during my investigations has a unique and different belief system towards spirits, hauntings, my work and my appearance. There are people in India who think I am some occult specialist or a voodoo teacher. Though India is opening up towards paranormal research and many educated people know what I am doing, usually in India it is a taboo to be associated with ghosts and spirits. I have also been treated badly by some families I visited to investigate. I have also met people afraid of talking to me because they believe that by doing so, they might attract negative entities or energies. On the other hand, I often meet people who treat me like a celebrity or a spiritual guru.'

'Come, I'll click a photo of you two,' Raj said.

'No, no. We will take a selfie. I want you in the photo too,' Bhadoria said. 'Sir, I wanted to contact you about something that I think might interest you. It's regarding my son.'

'Oh, he is a fan too?' Raj quipped, but saw that Bhadoria was now quite serious.

'Beta, come here,' Bhadoria turned and called out to a little boy in shorts, seated in a corner of the restaurant, sipping cola.

'Meet my son, Tarun. Beta, say hi to Gaurav uncle.'

The boy must have been about seven or eight years old.

'Hi, little boy.' Gaurav smiled and touched his cheek. Tarun smiled back.

There was something about Tarun that drew people to him. It probably didn't hurt that he was a good-looking boy, but it was more than that. He was quiet, but not out of shyness. It was more like he was reserved, like he was making a conscious choice to observe people around before he became more friendly. It wasn't like he had sat down one day and planned to be like that; it was just the way he was. He never went out and deliberately made a friend; they just came to him. There was nothing threatening about him, nothing at all. He was a good listener, giving encouraging feedback laced with intelligent comments; he was very mature for his age. Once in a while, he would sink into a sulk about some school work that he'd gotten wrong, and though it didn't happen to him often, he had poor tolerance for the feeling when it did.

'Sir, we think only you can help us. You are an expert in past life regression,' his father said.

Bhadoria said that Tarun was disturbed by his dreams. He could never recall what he'd seen in them, but it gave him a bad, bad feeling when he woke up. As a baby, he would cry often, but his parents thought this might be normal. All babies cry. But as he grew a little older and could make more sense of the world, he realised he had these nightmares almost daily. All he could remember when he woke up, sometimes in the morning but mostly in the night itself, with a jolt, was that they were depressing.

His father had taken him to a doctor who had tried to figure out the issue, but he'd given up and suggested that they consult a psychiatrist.

'Are you crazy? You think he is mad?'

'You don't need to be mad to see a psychiatrist, Mr Bhadoria. Mental health is important. What is happening to him could be due to a number of factors at home too,' the doctor had said.

But Bhadoria didn't think that was the case. They were a happy, supportive family, and there was no reason, he thought, for his son to have mental issues stemming from home life. A few months back, he had started following Gaurav Tiwari and his work. The more he read and saw about him, his cases, his articles, his shows, the more he understood one thing—there was something inexplicable about what was happening with his son. He had heard about reincarnation, but never believed in it till recently. Could that be the problem with his son? Only Gaurav could help.

'I've a confession, sir,' Bhadoria said.

'Yes?'

'I had been following your Facebook posts and knew you would be coming to Jaisalmer. We travelled from Jodhpur just yesterday, only to meet you.'

'Ah! And how did you know I was staying at this hotel?'

'Raj sir checked in, no? I saw that update on Facebook.' He smiled.

Gaurav and Raj looked at each other.

'Stalked for a reason. We need to help for sure.' Gaurav laughed at the innocence of Nishant Bhadoria, a worried father who had come to him for help.

Gaurav was an expert in past life regression therapy and had helped many people. He rarely talked about it, though. Past life regression therapy is a guided hypnosis in which memories of your past life or lives can be recovered for your betterment. Through this, people can figure out why certain things are haunting them and also reconnect with past life experiences—they can understand why they feel a deep connection with certain places, identify physical ailments they have that may be remnants of a past life and explore emotions that have been carried through into this lifetime due to their negative energies, often leading to fears and beliefs that are unexplainable.

While Raj and Bhadoria waited in the lobby, Gaurav took Tarun to his room and asked him to lie down on the bed.

'Tarun, you need to relax. Okay?' Gaurav said. Gaurav drew the curtains close and switched on a dim table lamp so Tarun would be more at ease. 'Do you hear the ticking of that device there?' he asked, pointing to a metronome. 'Close your eyes, clear all distractions from your mind, forget about everything. Just concentrate on what I tell you. Yes, bring your breathing to an even flow. Like this …' Gaurav showed him how to do it.

Sticking to the process is of utmost importance. Once the person achieves complete relaxation, it may feel like he or she is in a mild trance. This is very natural as the brain waves reach an alpha state. If the relaxation part is successful, the brain reaches a theta state—it is here that the mind is most open to past life memories as well as other kinds of psychic thoughts. This is when they can let the mind wander, although still listening to the guide's voice, which may sound very distant, but is still telling them where to go from there. None of the thoughts should be dismissed, as everything has a meaning, even if not explicit.

Memories don't work like cameras. Most of what we remember is a tapestry of experiences, feelings, or even something we saw on television, say, twenty years ago. They are cocktails of misplaced images and feelings. Or memories might be visions of a previous life as our soul makes another pit stop on the astral plane highway; that is our astral body having an out-of-body experience observing things while the mind is under hypnosis.

Tarun came out on the other side of the light feeling like he was alive, and at the same time, like he wasn't. An unreal experience but as real as anything can be. Gaurav's voice compelled him to simply remember, his words reverberating across the universe. He was first asked to describe himself as Tarun's astral body looked around, shifting between a first-person view and an out-of-body perspective.

They started from the bottom and worked their way up. The little boy, not little in this vision but a man, saw his bare feet in a dust-swept land. He saw his body draped in unfamiliar clothes. His outline was fuzzy, but his surroundings were crystal-clear: he was in a massive desert. He had a stick in one hand and a camel by his side.

As the voice continued to talk, asking questions, prodding Tarun about what he was feeling and what he was seeing, the story unfurled. While he felt himself 'inside' a body, he also saw himself in full-blown movie-montage mode. It was like all the moments of his life were happening at the same time.

He had a family—a wife and a daughter. He was respected in his circle. He was under an avalanche of pressure. He saw the big picture of his existence swelling around him effortlessly. He felt a lifetime of hardships. He experienced relationships that lasted years, some of which were with people who stabbed him in the back. He endured a famine. He loved his daughter more than anyone or anything in the world. He felt guilty. He took long walks. There wasn't any consistency in what he felt—there were many emotions all at the same time. He argued. He was celebrated, and ostracised. He watched the moon and stared slack-jawed at stars that don't exist anymore. He left for some place with his family after a terrible incident happened in his surroundings. He led a miserable life thereafter but tried hard to sustain and take care of his family. He cried. And when he died, he felt a river wash him away, hooking him by the hip and shooting him back to his creator, through a bottleneck of shining silver light.

'Where are you?' the voice asked.

'This … is somewhere in Rajasthan,' Tarun mumbled, but not in English or Hindi. It was a local dialect; perhaps Marwari with some influence of Hindi, hence comprehensible to Gaurav.

'Exact place? You will ask someone and tell me now,' Gaurav said, and repeated the sentence calmly.

'Khaba village near Jaisalmer,' Tarun replied after a pause.

Gaurav sat up. He controlled his emotion and asked, 'What happened there?'

Silence.

'I repeat. What happened there?'

His voice had become part of Tarun's consciousness. It wasn't Gaurav's voice; just a voice which came from within him while he was in some place he had lived many eons ago. The next moment he started to float above his body, with a string of lights hanging in the air below him. The string broke, sending the lights floating like a swarm of fireflies. He saw, among the many lights, an ethereal silver glow. He fluttered down to one and became absorbed in it.

'I'm waiting, Tarun.'

'Who Tarun?' he asked, slightly twitching his eyebrows.

'You, of course.'

'My name is Badri,' Tarun told him in Marwari, his voice sounding deeper.

'Okay, Badri. Tell me, what happened in Khaba?'

No answer.

'Badri …' Gaurav raised his voice a little.

The next moment, there was another silver glow and a flash. The only difference was that Gaurav saw it too and …

A gust of dry wind wound through the maze of ancient houses where windows had long been shattered in the weakness of their structures and rotting boards, most broken, some hanging, trying to cover the empty eyes of the long-abandoned homes. Doors hung on their hinges and groaned with pain with every sway. Weeds made their way through the cracking asphalt of every road, gathering and laughing at the lone pedestrian. Strangely, none of the houses in the ruins had roofs.

'Where am I? Which place is this?' Gaurav was quite baffled at what was transpiring in the past life regression session.

Gaurav looked around and realised he knew the place. He had seen the photos. It was the village near Khaba Fort. Yes, he could see it too. But how had he reached there? He had no memory of travelling from the hotel to the place. Moreover, he was alone and without his equipment. The world around felt the same, and yet different. The few trees stood naked with their twigs curled in a distorted way, as if they were screaming in pain. The sky was a mass of grey clouds, but instead of letting small shafts of light through, they emitted an ethereal glow. The wind was chilly and carried the scent of something peculiar, metallic almost, acrid.

'We lived here.' Badri's voice, which now felt like Gaurav's consciousness, could be heard.

The village looked very much like Kuldhara except for the fort on a nearby hill overlooking it. Gaurav climbed stairs to the fort's entrance and could feel a time when it was the focal point of a prosperous village. The turreted towers, elegant windows and intricate latticework served as a testament to the artistic talents of the Paliwal Brahmins. Once up there, Gaurav had a breathtaking view of the village and surrounding areas. Soon it started raining, but Gaurav continued to stand, the wind blowing through him.

There was an invisible force not letting him move an inch from where he stood.

'It rained just like this that day too ...' the voice said.

1845. The villagers in Kuldhara, Khaba and nearby villages were mostly agricultural traders, bankers and farmers. For agricultural purposes, the villagers used the water from the Kakni River and several wells. But by 1815, most of the wells had dried up and there was a severe water problem in the area. This was not the only reason for their unhappiness though. The diwan of Jaisalmer, Salim Singh, often referred to mockingly as 'Zaalim' Singh, an atrocious man, was attracted to a beautiful girl. He had even sent his guards to force villagers to hand over the girl to him when his advances were not reciprocated by her. Everyone stood strong and didn't allow that to happen. He then started levying excessive taxes on the villagers who were already bearing the brunt of the very low water supply. Eighty-four villages were abandoned due to this. Some say it was done on the same day, but the truth is it happened over the course of several years. There were only about seventy people who still lived there in 1845. Badri and his family were among them. The pain of their situation was so excruciating and intolerable that they had cursed the place—nobody would be able to live there after the last Paliwal Brahmin left the area.

'Uncle...uncle...'Tarun'svoiceseemedtobecomingfrom a distance.

'Gaurav!' Raj hugged him as he opened his eyes slowly.

'What happened here?' Bhadoria was in the room too.

'It was a very different past life regression experience

for me,' Gaurav said as he sat up, only half-aware of his surroundings, but trying to interpret what had happened.

'What's the time?' he asked Raj.

'1 p.m.'

'It's not even been an hour since I brought Tarun here, but it feels like a lifetime,' he said slowly, barely audible.

'Are you okay?' Raj was worried about his best friend. He offered him a glass of water, which Gaurav took and drank in one gulp. He was thirsty.

'This is what I feel. Badri's spirit, which was stuck between his death and his reincarnation, showed and told me what happened in Khaba through a vision.'

'Badri who?' Bhadoria and Raj asked at the same time. Gaurav explained it to them. He said he had been monitoring Tarun's past life regression till all of a sudden he became a part of it; it had never happened to him before.

Sometimes, after death, people with emotional baggage are stuck between the physical world and the light of salvation. For some, the time in the spirit realms may be relatively brief before they reincarnate; for others, it may be many hundreds of years. Each case is different. In each instance of life, we have the opportunity to improve our karmic pattern and the vibrations of our aura through the choices we make.

In the case of Tarun, the little boy had travelled back in time—first to his younger years, then his birth, then the spirit realm, before having those visions of his past life when he was Badri. Gaurav's voice had become his consciousness, and while the probing continued, Badri's spirit took the shape of Gaurav's consciousness.

'It's complicated. You won't understand the way we do, Mr Bhadoria. But all I can tell you now is that Tarun should be fine. His session went well, and he now has an idea of what's been bothering him all these years—remnants of his past life memories, some not so good ones. Do keep me updated.' Gaurav smiled and bid them goodbye.

Later that night they headed to Khaba Fort. On the way, they stopped to check if things had been sorted out for them. 'Saab, people don't return from that damned place in the morning if they stay there at night,' a local warned the team.

'We will break that myth. It's just a place with some very bad memories still latched onto it. We are not here to spread superstition. Please tell the others that,' Gaurav said and smiled at his team and the Zee News reporter, who were still tired after the Kuldhara case.

SIXTEEN

HAUNTED GOVERNMENT QUARTERS, MUMBAI

All black magic starts with an intention and is removed with stronger intention. No evil can ever survive the onslaught of positive thoughts.

— GAURAV TIWARI

May 2014

After ten years at his government job, Dattatray was being transferred from his hometown Satara to Mumbai. At first he had been very reluctant to take it up as there was never a doubt in his mind about where he wanted to live—Satara. But the thing with government jobs is that if one wants to grow, one has to be open to shifting and being based in different cities and towns.

Another dilemma was that his parents wanted him to get married, but he wasn't sure if he was ready financially. His salary was meagre compared to his friends who had moved to greener pastures after college. They all had one thing in common—none of them had stayed back in Satara. One day, all of a sudden, the realisation hit Dattatray hard, really hard. He was a few steps back in life. But there was still time. So he had taken the tough decision to move out of Satara. He would miss his parents and the place. Damn! Panchgani and Mahabaleshwar were so close! He used to go there with his colleagues almost every weekend. Yes, he would miss them, but they kept being transferred as well—most of them. Some preferred to remain clerks and relish life as it was. *It's sad that towns are not the place for people with big dreams*, he thought. *People have to compromise, move around and live their entire lives wishing they could make it back to their homes. Alas, most of them never get to do that. Responsibilities pile up over the years and you tend to make a home out of the place you were once a stranger to.*

But to make things better for Dattatray, his sister Vasudha would be staying with him in Mumbai. She was the complete opposite of him. Eleven years younger, she had always known Satara wasn't the place for her and had moved to Mumbai right after her school exams, two years ago. She was now in her second year of college, also working part-time.

'Wow, Dada! I'm so happy we can stay together,' she had said when he called and told her about his decision.

'Yes, my little sis! I'll feel at home!'

'Yeah! And I can save on rent.'

'Ah! I see. That's why you are happy, huh!'

'Ha ha! Rents are sky-high here, Dada. How would you know? Sarkaari and all!'

'Ha ha, true. By the way, the flat is in Kandivali.'

'Cool. Works well for me too. My college and office are both in Andheri, so travelling won't be much of an issue. There is a direct train.'

'Great.'

'Welcome to Mumbai, Dada!' Vasudha said, elated that she would have family with her.

In a few weeks, Dattatray was in Mumbai and given the key to his government quarters, a stone's throw from where he would have to report daily. Vasudha had vacated her one-room-kitchen flat in Goregaon by this time.

'Let's order some food for dinner, shall we? We can buy the necessary stuff tomorrow and the maid should join us then,' Dattatray said.

'Let's have pizza today. My treat!' Vasudha said.

Dattatray smiled at his little sister. It felt like just yesterday when he had seen her as a toddler, and here she was now, treating him with her hard-earned money. She was not little anymore and he had to accept it.

The residence for the government employees of the telecom organisation was a complex comprising four buildings and a lawn in between. Each building had four floors, three flats on each of them. Earlier that day, when they had moved into the flat allotted to Dattatray, the siblings had observed many oil stains in one of the rooms, especially on the cupboards and the ceiling. It was as if someone used to light many oil lamps there. Vasudha tried her best to clean the place, but not all of it could be removed. When the security guard was asked about it, he only remarked that it was an old place.

A few days later, they had settled down in the apartment. Dattatray had begun going to his office as well. Since his office was so close by, he left home long after his sister and got back before her. Vasudha would leave early in the morning to attend a few lectures, after which she went to her office. During evening peak hours, it took Vasudha at least an hour just to reach Andheri station—this was before the metro became operational in the city.

One night, Vasudha wasn't able to sleep well. There was too much going on in her head—the pressure of studies and examinations, the part-time job and a failed relationship with a guy in college which she hadn't told anyone about. It was around 1 a.m.; she had been tossing and turning, trying hard to sleep by listening to some melodious music. It was a hot and humid night. They hadn't bought an air conditioner yet, and the fan didn't help much, so they had kept the door to the balcony adjoining the bedroom open. It was just a concrete ledge with rough edges and a rusty rail, but it was Vasudha's oasis. She had filled the space with potted plants and was waiting to see the riot of colours when the time was right.

Now, as she turned again, trying to get comfortable, she thought she could see a shadow on the balcony. She rubbed her eyes and looked again. She had seen right. There was someone standing in the balcony! Then the figure walked forward. It was a lady … wearing a nightgown …

Vasudha sat up, but even before she could utter anything, it vanished into thin air.

'Dada!' Vasudha screamed, waking up Dattatray in the next room.

'Come on, you can't be serious,' he said when she'd told him what she'd seen.

'I am, Dada! I'm sure about what I saw.'

'Could it not be that you fell asleep and dreamt it, then woke up with a jolt and found yourself sitting on the bed?'

Vasudha thought he had a point and calmed down.

But the next night she saw her again, and this time her brother had no option but to believe it …

Vasudha had insisted Dattatray stay in the same room as her, and as he was preparing to go to sleep at 10 p.m., like he did daily, there was a sound.

'Did you hear that?' Vasudha whispered, straining her ears.

Dattatray sat up. Yes, he had heard it. He couldn't lie to himself. It was like the tinkling of anklets—very faint at first, then it got clearer, and then even clearer, till they felt there was someone in the bedroom. Someone seemed to be walking from the bedroom door to the balcony; the tinkling became clearer, but there was nobody to be seen.

'Wh-who is it?' Dattatray stuttered.

It stopped.

'Who is it?' Vasudha asked shakily.

There was a giggle. It sounded more like a mocking laugh. And then they both saw her—the lady in the gown standing in the balcony with her back to them.

The siblings trembled in fear as the entity disappeared right in front of their eyes the next second.

Over the course of the next few days, the strange activities became more frequent. Utensils fell down in the kitchen and they also witnessed shadows in the bedroom; often it felt like someone was standing right there watching them. Finally, Dattatray talked to the neighbours and learnt about the previous tenant, a lady named Trishana.

It turned out that most of the neighbours had the same opinion about Trishana—that she had been very strange; she had rarely spoken to anyone, had kept to herself, and had barely ever moved out of the house. Nobody really knew what she had been up to inside the flat. She had left all of a sudden and nobody knew where she had gone. Dattatray was also informed that a lady staying right next to their flat had committed suicide.

'Here, call this number. I got it from a client of mine, a lady here in Kandivali itself, who was being haunted by her past. I think only she can help you,' one of the neighbours said.

'Who is this?' Dattatray asked.

'Meghna Porwal. She works with the Indian Paranormal Society. Gaurav Tiwari? Rings a bell?' the neighbour asked.

What can make a leader happier than his team members being recognised for their work? All Gaurav's protégés had begun to make a name for themselves by then, and he was more than glad. He couldn't be available to investigate all the cases that came to them, but he had complete confidence in his people who represented IPS.

Meghna reached the government quarters a little early and waited downstairs for her team. She would meet the clients only with her team. It was one of the many things she had learnt from Gaurav. Soon, Siddharth, Rith and Mohan joined her and they went up to meet Dattatray. Vasudha was on her way back from the office—she had informed them that she would reach in an hour at the most.

A day ago, Siddharth had paid them a visit and taken a baseline reading—a quick verification if the place should be investigated. The EMF meter reading had documented a few spikes and it could be determined that the place needed more probing and a cleansing too.

'How do you begin and go about things?' Dattatray asked.

'Simple. We communicate with the entity,' Meghna said and instructed the team to keep the equipment ready. She herself started taking photographs.

Siddharth attempted to set up an intelligent communication pattern with the entity and was successful.

'If you are male, reply with one beep. If female, two,' he said.

Two beeps on the EMF meter.

'Is there something you want to tell us?'

Beep!

Meghna continued taking a series of photos and was able to capture an anomaly in one of them—a shadowy figure in the room with the oil stains.

'Something bad used to happen here …' she whispered and showed the photograph to Dattatray and her team.

The doorbell rang. It was Vasudha.

Meghna showed her the picture in which she had captured the anomaly and Dattatray told her about what had happened so far.

Siddharth was still communicating with the entity. The spikes on the EMF were more frequent by now and it was understood that the spirit had something to say.

'This is creepy, Dada.'

'I'll not let anything happen to you, don't worry,' Dattatray said and asked her not to get too close to where the investigation was happening.

'Some negative energy has conjured up something here or invited spirits,' Meghna informed the siblings while taking a short coffee break.

Other residents in the building had already informed Dattatray that there had been some suspicions that evil rituals were practised there by the earlier tenant.

'Will the cleansing help, Meghna?' Dattatray asked almost pleadingly.

'Depends. I think it should, but the spirit or spirits have to give in. That's how it works. We aren't exorcists. Let me clarify here that it does not pertain to any religion; we simply communicate with the energy, try and understand why it is in that phase. Then we try to resolve things without causing any problem to anyone—be it the living or the dead. Empathy for them is of utmost importance and we humans tend to miss this point.' She took one last sip of her coffee and stood up.

'And what if she doesn't accept? There must be a reason she is here.' Vasudha looked worried.

'Don't worry. We are here to do our best. Siddharth, how's it going?' Meghna commenced with her work again.

'The lady who reportedly committed suicide … didn't actually! There was probably more to it but …'

'But what, Siddharth?'

'The communication has stopped.'

'Can I try?' Rith asked.

It was around 10.30 p.m. then. Dattatray's phone rang. All the mobile phones had been switched off except for Dattatray's, which he'd kept in the drawing room, away from where the investigations were being conducted. He went to pick it up and was confused to see that it was his sister calling him.

Must have called by mistake, he thought. He disconnected and placed the phone where it was.

'Vasudha …' he called out for her as he walked to the dining room where he had left her. But she wasn't there.

'Meghna …'

The phone rang again. Dattatray went back and picked it up.

'Dada, there was a huge jam! Tell me, should I get some food from the restaurant downstairs?'

'What …' Dattatray was too baffled to make sense of what was going on.

'*Damn …*' Siddharth gave a loud cry. They all ran to the room with the oil stains, which was where he was.

'I thought I saw someone sitting here for a split second,' he told them as they rushed to check on him, pointing at the place where the oil stains were.

Dattatray looked around and froze …

The lady in the gown was standing there, right in front of his eyes! She stood still, facing him; only the movement of her hair gave away that it was not some brilliant Halloween decoration.

The ghost stared at him with wide eyes, her face passive and slack. After a moment of indecision coupled with utter fear, Dattatray took a step backward and turned to run. The door slammed shut. The lights went off. Although the moonlight was bright outside, it did not penetrate the glass. The clock ceased to tick. There seemed to be no sound from the outside world. Then the air was rent with a scream that was so piercing that Dattatray collapsed to the floor in a foetal position, his hands clamped to his ears … not that it made any difference. The air became cold and his body heat quickly deserted him. An awareness crept over him that he was no longer in contact with the ground but instead, spinning. Once he opened his eyes, the room was no longer there; instead, there was the ghost's face and open mouth that had become magnified. In utter paralysis, he was drawn towards it. Dattatray screamed at the top of his voice. The next moment …

'Are you okay?' Meghna's voice snapped Dattatray out of his vision.

Thirty minutes later …
Vasudha had returned by then and had been briefed about what had happened during her absence.

'The lady who lived here … Trishana …' Meghna said after noting down a few points on her phone, which she would need to mention in the report after the post-investigation work. 'She practised certain rituals which you can obviously make out from the oil stains in that room.'

'Ye-yes,' Dattatray said, still reeling from what he had experienced.

'There is more to this place. The incident next door has something to do with it. As Siddharth pointed out, it might not have been a suicide. You see, entities don't always communicate in entirety.'

'Move out of here. We will still do some more cleansing here over the next few days, but please see if you can move. We want you to be safe,' Rith said.

'There is more than one spirit here. Many more for sure, mostly unleashed during the rituals that happened here,' Siddharth said.

The team bid the siblings goodbye and left. Both were in a state of shock, and it was only after a counselling session with the IPS team later on that they felt better.

'Spooky feeling in there, huh!' Rith lit a cigarette when they were outside.

'Mohan, you make the report this time. We will mail you the points after analysing the recordings. Damn, my phone ...' Siddharth suddenly remembered he had left his phone in the flat. He rushed back up, collected his phone, bid them goodbye once again and took the stairs. He could sprint down rather than wait for the lift which was stuck on the second floor.

'Never come back here ...' he heard a lady's voice echo.

A startled Siddharth looked around. In the dimly lit place, there was an old lady sitting on one of the steps, mumbling something. He went up to her and asked, 'Did you say something?'

She had pitch-black eyes that reminded him of coal. Her hair was long and stringy. Siddharth looked closely at what she was holding in her hands. It was a photograph of Gaurav. The old lady looked up at Siddharth and smiled wickedly.

Just then, the bulbs that were the only source of light in the stairwell exploded one after the other as Siddharth stood there, almost paralysed, till there was complete darkness.

The next moment, everything was normal, just the way it had been earlier. There was no old lady there, and all the bulbs were working.

Siddharth called Gaurav the next day to discuss this vision he'd had.

'Sometimes, they perform certain activities to tell you they exist. Sometimes these visions may be premonitions, indicating something might happen soon. Don't worry about it. Tell me, how did the investigation go?'

Siddharth briefed him and said they would be visiting the place again later that week for the cleansing activities. They would monitor the progress and then intimate Dattatray and Vasudha if there were any other possible resolutions.

'Good, my boy. You know I've cut down on travelling, but did I tell you I'm not worried at all? I have a team that I'm extremely confident about and proud of. It's that phase for me where I have blind faith in all of you, Siddharth.'

'We will never let you down, sir. Ever.' Siddharth smiled. His day was made.

SEVENTEEN

THE HAUNTED APARTMENT IN DELHI

The 'survival hypothesis' is a theory that states a person's personality and consciousness survive the physical death of the body. That means we will have the same emotions, same pain, anger, love, hatred, etc., even after death. That being said, a good person in life will be a good person after death. A bully in life will be a bully after his death.

— GAURAV TIWARI

June 2016 (one month before Gaurav's death)

Some people revel in the sensory calm that being alone brings. Gaurav was one such person for sure; he found himself at his creative best when in solitude. But this was a phase when being all by himself was probably his worst nightmare. He didn't really say this to anyone explicitly. That wasn't his style. Gaurav kept a lot of things to himself, and even the person closest to him wouldn't know what was going on in his mind. He sometimes took solace in his imagination; a fort that only he could enter. He kept himself tremendously busy with cases so that an idle mind did not become the devil's workshop. But spirits were real—both good ones and bad ones. It's all in the mind who you let win at the end of the day. Gaurav's battle was real too, and nobody could really comprehend it; nobody could read his mind. He had always been unpredictable and this very attribute of his made it difficult for his family and friends to guess what was in store for all of them.

During this time, Gaurav—quite unusually for him— used to prefer investigating cases on his own. He had stopped travelling to other locations, but even in Delhi, there were times when he would not accompany Raj for cases. He told him that it was important that he spend more time at home than he had earlier.

'I guess it's important to balance personal and professional lives,' he had told him once.

Siddharth was in Delhi then for a few months to learn from his mentor, and he noted that Gaurav was busy with work as usual. The only difference was that he would visit places alone. Also, there were days when he spent more time with Siddharth at the office than with Raj, who was a very close friend. Raj himself had become busier than usual. The number of requests for investigations had shot up over the years. This was when IPS was actually at its peak. In fact, many people, mostly youngsters, inspired by Gaurav, took a cue and began their own investigation teams. Some of these groups didn't meet standards though, and damaged the reputation of legitimate investigators. It irked Gaurav, but when he was asked to comment on this by news channels, he refrained from being too vocal.

'Your work will speak for itself. Nothing else matters. The good, bad, ugly part will be exposed over the years,' he had said once.

It had been over a fortnight since Raj had met Gaurav because he had travelled to Bhopal for work related to his business.

He called him one evening. '*Bhai, bahut din ho gaye. Milte hain* (Brother, it's been many days since we have met. Let's meet)?'

'*Haan, bade log! Aap ke paas samay kaha hain hum se milne ke liye* (You are a busy man! Why will you meet me)?' Gaurav had teased.

'Okay, okay. Don't pull my leg now. I'll pick you up tomorrow afternoon. Let's catch up over some snacks and drinks. What say?'

'Yeah. Drinks like Thums Up for me.'

The night before the much-awaited get-together, Raj had a case to investigate. He would be going alone. Little did he know that it would turn out to be one of his most spine-chilling cases ...

Malti was a single mother living with her son and daughter in Ghaziabad. She had moved there from Greater Kailash after divorcing her husband. Property rates were cheaper there, and though the place was infamous for not being safe after dusk, she had decided to take the risk. It was a posh apartment that she had bought at quite an affordable price. Also, her office in Noida was not too far away from there, so she felt it was a good decision.

Along with the three of them, there was a full-time maid in the house who helped take care of her children—six-year-old Ratul and two-year-old Tiasha. It was a spacious 3 BHK flat—well-planned, modern and very cool. Nothing could ever have hinted at any sort of a haunting.

Everything was okay for the first few days after they moved in, until one night …

Malti was working on her laptop. She had a presentation to make for a client the next morning, and she had not been able to work on it at the office as there had been back-to-back meetings and conference calls. It must have been around 11 p.m. Her kids had gone to sleep and so had the maid, Dolly.

Malti heard some noises coming from the dining room, which was where Dolly preferred to sleep at night as she found it comfortable. Malti saved the PowerPoint presentation she was working on and, quite sleepily, walked towards where the noises were getting louder. She saw the fridge door was open, and in the light emitting from it, she could see someone sitting near it.

'Dolly, is that you?' she asked.

The noises stopped.

'Dolly—' Malti stopped short. She was staring at someone who looked exactly like her, with uncooked meat in her hands that she had been devouring. The person who looked like Malti smiled devilishly at her.

'Look, we have enough food out here.' She pointed at the fridge stocked with human flesh—someone's decapitated head lay on the upper tray, other body parts elsewhere and fresh blood dripped from the meat.

Malti woke up with a jolt and realised it was a nightmare. She sat up on the bed, reached for the water bottle on her bedside table, poured it into a glass and drank it in one gulp, breathing heavily. She looked around to see her laptop had still not shut down. She couldn't remember it, but she guessed she must have felt sleepy and thought of taking a short nap. Obviously she had fallen into a deep sleep.

'I need to complete this presentation, or I'm screwed tomorrow,' she complained to herself and reluctantly got out of bed.

Just as she sat on the chair and was about to resume her work, there was a loud banging noise on the glass window. The mirror in front of her cracked and Malti looked at it. She was looking at her reflection, but she looked different— her eyes were different, her skin, her face … it was more a white cloud-like figure with eyes and a mouth as black as the night sky.

'I'll soon become you … and this is no dream,' it whispered and laughed at Malti who blacked out the next second.

Malti got in touch with the IPS the very next day and spoke to Raj. As much as Raj loved to work with his team, he was also a daredevil. A very confident man in general, when it came to things related to the unknown, Raj enjoyed pushing the envelope. He still does. So when Malti briefed him about what had happened, Raj decided to carry out the investigation alone; in any case, her home was close to where he resided then.

'So, do we go and stay in some hotel tonight while you check the apartment out?' Malti asked Raj after exchanging pleasantries.

'No, no. Stay. I'm here. You need not worry at all.' He unpacked his equipment, educating her about the use of each of the gadgets as he did so.

'Seems genuine,' she said.

'Absolutely. There is no room for manipulation in our approach. By the end of this session, you will understand. It's all scientific and I'll even document the same and mail it to you.'

Raj switched on the EVP recorder and picked up the full-spectrum camera.

'You hold this,' he told Malti, handing her an EMF meter which had already begun spiking.

There had been no breeze outside when he had entered the building. Nor were any of the windows in the flat open. Yet, once Raj entered and the door heaved to a close, there was a howl, soft and whining. Given the lingering heat of summer, the drawing room was surprisingly cold, enough to raise the hair on his arms. As Raj moved through the door to one of the bedrooms, he thought he heard laughter—not a happy laugh though, more of a snigger.

'Are your children inside?' he asked.

'No, I didn't want to take that chance. They are at a neighbour's place.'

'Do you hear what I hear? Do you feel what I feel?'

'I … I don't quite get you. What …'

'Never mind. I'll explain later.'

Once they were over the threshold of Malti's bedroom where the incident had occurred, Raj stood for a moment and looked at the mirror.

'Do you know mirrors are never to be placed opposite where you sleep?' he asked Malti.

'No. But why?'

'It is believed that mirrors are portals to *the other world.*'

'*The other world?*'

'Yes. In simple words, the world of the dead.'

The very next second, the door slammed shut behind them. They jerked around. There was no breeze that could have caused that. Then the lock clicked. The windows transformed into a solid wall and, with their disappearance, Raj felt his head spinning. The lights went out and he could see nothing now. Before he could say anything, he felt his mouth seal shut. Eyes appeared in the blackness with no form and then the apparition of a gaunt man appeared before him, first faint and then almost as solid as a flesh and blood person. He smiled and rubbed his hands together.

'You are at the wrong place,' he snarled.

Raj remembered he had a lighter in his pocket. He lit it.

'Ms Malti, are you there?' he asked. But there was nobody there. His voice echoed. Was he even in the same apartment he had come to investigate? It certainly didn't feel like it. Raj strained his eyes and tried to locate where the switches were. When he spotted them, he walked there slowly. He was almost near it when someone blew out the flame of the lighter.

'Get the hell out of here,' someone whispered in both his ears.

The sound of a child screaming emerged from the momentary silence after the whisper. At first it was distant but it came steadily closer, all the while becoming more intense, more distressed, until it was undeniably in the house itself. Then it all stopped and there was an eerie silence. The clicking of locks could be heard. The windows that had disappeared a while ago were now replaced by a view of gallows on a starlit night. The lights came on, then flickered and went out. Then, from the gloom, there stepped the same gaunt man, rubbing his hands together, his white frozen lips pulled tight over broken teeth. Taking a step forward, he opened his crooked mouth to speak. 'I have a son who is dependent on me. Please spare me.'

'Your appeal is denied. You will be hanged till death at sunrise,' someone said.

The man screamed, the noise accompanied by the high-pitched cry of his child … it grew louder with every second! Raj stood there unable to move even an eyelid, as if he was paralysed. He heard their pain, felt it; felt it in his heart.

A ghost is but an emotion—be it happy, sad, angry—twisted out of shape. It wants to make its presence felt and there are times when it also wants you to feel what it feels, to undo what wrong might have happened when it breathed.

'Mr Raj … Mr Raj …' Malti woke him up with a nudge.

'What …' Raj sat up and looked around. He heard the clock ticking and realised he was sweating profusely.

'What time …' he tried hard to be audible, but he was still not completely in his senses. He understood he'd had a vision and the entity or entities in the apartment had communicated to him via it.

'It's 3.35.'

'I don't … remember …' He noticed he was in a different room than the one he'd been in, and there was another woman with Malti.

'She is my maid, Dolly,' Malti said. She told him they had brought him to the guest room when he'd been unconscious.

Raj stood up, asked the ladies to follow him out of the apartment and hurried to take the lift downstairs.

'Mr Raj … is everything okay?' Malti said as they sat on a bench in the lawn.

'This place is one of the creepiest I've come across, really. But the presence has a purpose and I'll calm it,' Raj said and collected his equipment from Dolly who had brought it downstairs.

'We will need to cleanse your house soon and I'm hoping things will be fine then.'

The visions Raj had had were real. They were basically a visit to *the other world* through his astral body which had wandered off to find out about the place and its curse.

'What is your flat number, Malti?'

'B-602. Why?'

'I did some research about this place before I came. Did you know that your flat number and the house number of the property that was sold to the real estate developers are the same?'

She shook her head. 'No. But why is that important?'

'I had a vision back up there … and let me tell you it was malefic.' He told the two of them what he'd seen and continued with his findings, joining the dots of whatever he had seen or heard in the vision. Google also helped.

Sometime in the early 1990s, a man was supposedly falsely accused of a murder and hanged to death. He had pleaded not guilty and said he was being framed by some influential people. But nothing had helped. A few days after his execution, his only child, a six-year-old boy, was found dead outside the house. Apparently, he was run over by a truck. Some said the man's younger brother had something to do with what had happened as he had wanted to sell the property and move abroad with his family. But there was no evidence to back this theory. After the deaths, the brother and his family had shifted to South Delhi and lived there for a few years in a rented place. When the property was sold off for a hefty amount of money, they had moved abroad. House number B-602 was soon demolished and the construction of an upscale complex of two high-rises had begun in 2005. There were a few paranormal incidents during this period too, but the developers and promoters obviously didn't mention them to anyone to avoid any sort of issue while selling the flats. If a few labourers who worked there are to be believed, a co-worker had died there due to an unexplained occurrence. His family was bribed and asked to keep quiet about it. No FIR was ever lodged.

The man and his son's spirits haunted the place and it could be ascertained why activities were probably more where Malti resided. Her flat was the house number. B-602!

The next day, Raj woke up a little late, sent an official mail to Malti about his findings and his suggestions, took a shower and drove straight to Dwarka where Gaurav lived.

He would go over to Malti's house on the weekend for a cleansing.

'I'll be there in a jiffy,' Gaurav said over the phone as Raj waited in his car, listening to one of his favourite songs. He loved (and still enjoys) humming along to romantic numbers and was in a mood to unwind with his best friend.

'*Bhai, aapke to darshan durlabh ho gaye* (Rarely do I get to see you these days, brother)!' Raj said as Gaurav got into his car.

'*Shaadi to kar beta, phir samjhega* (You will know when you get married)!'

'Find me a girl. I will.'

'That will be tough, man! Wonder who will marry a blunt guy like you!' Gaurav joked.

'Why are you keeping so much to yourself these days?' Raj asked him as they ordered snacks at their favourite hangout.

'But I've always been like this, no?' Gaurav smiled.

Raj studied his friend's eyes, which were very expressive. They spoke then too. There was something bothering Gaurav for sure, but he wouldn't tell.

'Allen called,' Gaurav said, changing the subject. Allen and Gaurav were like brothers.

'The other day we chatted on Facebook Messenger. Cool guy. I have to meet him one day.'

'So he wants me to pay a visit to Australia again, but this time, not to investigate for *Haunting: Australia*.'

'Then?'

'There is a Ted Talk-styled lecture tour that will be held there next month.'

'Ah, you are already a speaker at Ted Talk.'

'Yeah. But there is more to it. He wants us to collaborate and write a book together.'

'Whoa! That's nice. You want to?'

'Yes, yes. Why not? I want more and more people to know about us, about Indian Paranormal Society. He was also talking about a new television show.'

'You should go.'

'Let's see ...' Gaurav said and paused for a while. Raj looked at his friend. He seemed oddly distrait.

'All good, buddy? You can tell me if there is anything ... Look—'

'All good, all good. A lot to do! Come on, let's have some beer today.'

'Great! Cheers!'

They had a good time, a very good time—and it was the last time really that Gaurav and Raj spent time together. Raj did meet him once more before Gaurav passed away, but it was for a very brief time.

'It's been so many years since 2009 and IPS still remains ... a primary resource recognised in India as a frontrunner in the anomalous research field by providing online training, resources, a forum and a database of credible paranormal and anomalous evidence. Have I quoted you right there? Got that from a few notes I made. Here, you can have a look.' I showed them a part of my research notes.

Meghna and Siddharth looked at my notes and nodded. 'Yes, that's right,' Meghna said.

'So tell me, I want to hear from the pioneers of paranormal investigation in India. What keeps you relevant after so many years, even after Gaurav's untimely demise?'

'Hmm, I guess it's our passion to unearth the truth and nothing but the truth using the most genuine methods, and all of them scientific.'

'Great. Let me make a note of this too. I want the book to be authentic, and here's hoping I can do justice to your journey and Gaurav Tiwari.'

I paused and then continued. 'There's one thing I wanted to ask … Can I accompany you on an investigation, or maybe I could join you to call spirits of the departed someday? It's been a childhood wish! As much as I'm fascinated by ghosts, I've not seen one yet. I've tried—but alas!'

'They are everywhere, Abhirup. Even now, as we speak, they must be here. Their world and ours run parallel to each other. Sure, we will involve you when possible!' Meghna said with a smile and asked Siddharth to get some tea from a nearby vendor.

'Let's hope he has opened his shop after the night's rain!' Siddharth said and walked out of the room.

I looked out of the window. It had stopped raining. I wondered for a moment how often we people see the dawn and take the sun for granted, we see the blackness become a vista, the world we love, our home—yet after that, do we think of the light and how it brings our world to life? Do we think about how it shows us colour instead of only grey, and warms us from our skin to our core, ignites our thoughts to beauty, inviting that light and warmth to enter our hearts, before respectfully giving us time to dream, giving us the moon and the stars? As the sky changes from charcoal to soft dove grey and you happen to see it, cherish the blue that is to come. For the dawn is the invitation to the day, to the gift that is the present, if we live and love well with gratitude. It is the proof that after every darkness, there is light; along with evil, good exists in the same world.

I switched off my laptop, put my notebook in my bag and stood up. 'I'll take your leave, Meghna.'

'Wait for tea ...'

'Some other day. I need to get working on the book now. Like NOW!' I said and left.

I knew that once Siddharth returned, he and Meghna would probably talk about their next case. The work would go on. It always did, with Gaurav guiding them when he had been alive, as well as now, from the afterlife. He continues to live through his team and the work they do.

EPILOGUE

Cockatoo Island, Australia. It used to be a prison for people convicted of serious crimes in the early 1800s, and was later also used as a reformatory. It is famously haunted, and was first investigated by the *Haunting: Australia* team along with Gaurav. The most famous ghost there is that of the 'lady in red', who was probably the wife of the superintendent.

Gaurav entered the Biloela House (a house at the centre of the island) with EMF meters. He began communicating, asking the spirit(s) to light up the EMF meters and established communication with the spirit of the lady in red. She started lighting the meters on command.

Gaurav then asked her to light up the meter on the right if she had lost a child, and the light turned on the right meter. He then said, if she had lost a girl child she could answer by giving two beeps on the meter kept on the window. She did! He then asked the spirit to use the meters to reply 'yes' or 'no'—if 'yes', the meter in front of him; and if 'no', the meter on the right.

'Do you want help?'

The spirit replied with a no.

'Do you want to be alone?'

The spirit lit up the meter in front of him—yes.

'We all want to be alone, at times.' Gaurav smiled. He enjoyed being alone too. It was only then that he found himself the most productive.

I stared at my laptop screen for one whole minute, mulling over what I'd written, wondering if I should start the book here.

No. I knew where I needed to begin. Where it all started—the transformation of a young non-believer into a believer who would go on to achieve so much in the field of paranormal investigation and be an inspiration to so many people.

A FINAL WORD

— ALLEN TILLER

In August 2013, the *Haunting: Australia* cast and crew visited the Blue Mountains in New South Wales to film an outing and the reveal for the Woodford Academy episode of the show. The idea for the 'outing' segment was that ghost hunting-themed shows are predominantly filmed indoors but could, in fact, be anywhere. If we visited places of interest and had the cast participate in the outings, we could showcase Australia and create a point of difference from other television shows.

We arrived at the historic town of Katoomba and were taken to the Fairmont Resort to ride Segways—something none of the cast wanted to do as most of us were worried we would get injured. We were quickly trained on how the vehicles worked. We were then taken to a path alongside a valley to ride the Segways—a very long drop if one were to make a mistake. The camera crews set up in three locations along the path. We would ride in a row in one direction, turn around and go the other way. We did this so many times that I lost count. On the last turn, I ended up at the front of the line with Ray Jordan behind me, then Gaurav, Ian, Rayleen and Robb. I sped along the path, and I could hear Gaurav and Robb shouting at Ray to hurry up. I heard a thud but continued to the oval, our turnaround point. Nobody arrived behind us, but Ray and I could hear laughter from behind on the track.

A few moments later we were told Gaurav had met with an accident. As he was riding along, he had sped up behind Ray and tried to slow down, but ended up pivoting his Segway. Gaurav put his leg out to balance himself and hit a pine post that was cemented into the ground, breaking his leg just below his kneecap.

He was carried onto the oval and received medical treatment before being rushed off to the hospital.

If you watch the episode closely, you will see that Gaurav is at the front of the line. You will also hear the narrator blaming me for the incident when this was not the case at all. To make matters worse, with Gaurav gone, we were forced to complete filming the segment without him, and with no updates on his condition.

We completed the needed scenes at the resort and headed towards Mount Victoria. On the way there, we got some news that made the cast incredibly angry, and that would have ongoing repercussions which almost ended the filming (and the show). We were told Gaurav had been left at the hospital all by himself; even the producer, who was supposed to be there, wasn't with him. Gaurav had no idea where he was; he was without a phone, he had no passport or other identification proofs, and English was his second language. He told me later he spent close to six hours sitting there waiting for a doctor, not understanding what was really going on, before someone from the production crew turned up to see how he had been keeping. To say that he was ropeable was an understatement. So was the cast.

While Gaurav was at the hospital, the rest of the cast travelled to the nearby Mount Vic Flicks at Mount Victoria in the Upper Blue Mountains. The building opened in 1934, screening movies until the 1950s. It then remained closed until 1986, when it was reopened by Ron and Diane Bayley. Mount Victoria is allegedly haunted by the 'woman in black', Caroline Collett. It was because of the local hauntings that the location was chosen for our 'reveal'.

It was at this historic theatre that we first saw Gaurav again, after his shocking accident on the Segway at the Fairmont Resort.

In 2015, Gaurav returned to Australia. He told me that his leg had never really recovered, and he was still in pain from that accident. We revisited the Woodford Academy. For all of us, this visit was much better than our initial visit in 2013, as we were able to enjoy the scenery, the history and the building without the stress of being on camera, and the pressure of an executive producer barking orders at the cast, but having no idea how a ghost investigation works.

There are many more stories about working with Gaurav and the adventures we had that I could tell, and perhaps, one day, I will tell them. Instead, here I wanted to share an encounter with Gaurav, hopefully not my last.

7 July 2016
I woke up and got out of bed. As I left my room, my teenage daughter Chantelle was waiting in the hallway.

She asked me, 'Have you heard about Gaurav?'

I said, 'No, I just woke up. What happened?'

She informed me about his death; she had read it online.

I went into my office and turned the computer on.

'There are many people named Gaurav Tiwari in India,' I assured myself. It could as well be any other Gaurav Tiwari. Couldn't be my brother. Why would he die? How could he?

I logged into Facebook and saw countless messages asking me if I knew what was going on. There was a message from Robb Demarest, stating that it was true that Gaurav was dead, but that the details were sketchy.

Next, I heard from Gaurav's father directly that he was no more. I offered my sympathies to Mr Tiwari and his family, then silently mourned my little brother.

That night, at around 11 p.m., I was preparing to go to bed with a very heavy heart, still crying for my loss. In our house, we have a one-half bathroom with a toilet and hand basin, and adjacent to it, a full bathroom. I used the toilet, washed my hands, and as I opened the door, I could see Gaurav standing in front of the hand basin in the main bathroom. He was wearing a white robe with an orange sash that hung from his left shoulder, down his body. He looked me in the eye and smiled, right after which he disappeared. I had a sense that he was perfectly okay where he was. We often told each other that if one of us was to die earlier, we would contact the other to prove that life after death is real. (This is why I no longer try to prove the paranormal to anyone anymore, really. I know the afterlife is real, and that we can only perceive it from our own perspective, understanding, knowledge and experience.)

In 2019, I held a public investigation event at the Old Geelong Gaol. Gaurav and I had investigated the gaol for *Haunting: Australia*, and again in 2015 with the *Haunting: Australia* team. I had an idea that I may be able to contact Gaurav in spirit at this location. I asked Gaurav's team member and friend Meghna Porwal if she could translate a few words in Hindi for me that I could then play as a trigger object, to guide Gaurav to speak to me. I got more than I had bargained for.

I had set up the Project Paranormal application through a speaker system designed by Bros Overton. On the second investigation, the system kept shutting down. A psychic at the investigation claimed Gaurav was shutting it down, but the truth was I had not charged the unit correctly the night before (which I didn't know until consulting Bros Overton after the investigation).

Two psychics, Dani and Melanie, who had come along as guests, later pulled me aside as they said Gaurav was in the gaol and wanted to speak with me. I am a very sceptical person by nature, but I am not a non-believer; rather, I am a believer who is sceptical of anything that is told to me which I either do not experience for myself or do not have legitimate evidence to back up the claim. I have also taught myself many of the techniques psychics use, such as cold reading, cue and leading questions, and other forms of signalling that allow them to convince people they are talking to the dead, when, in fact, the customer is just giving the psychic the answers. You could say I was well prepared to be entertained by fake psychic babble, but this was not to be the case!

We stood at the bottom of the stairs in the East Wing, away from other guests. One of the psychics told me Gaurav was present and wanted to tell me something. On asking them what, they told me a few things that anyone who had followed Gaurav's life could have known, but in the middle of one sentence, one of them said something that very few people knew. I listened carefully and then told them to ask Gaurav to prove he was present by pulling my hair. I suddenly had my hair pulled; not a slight movement, but a forceful tug over my right shoulder. I checked no one was behind me and that my hair was not caught in my clothing. It was not.

I then started asking very vague questions, purposefully leaving out certain information. Melanie took the lead. She gave me details about Gaurav's wife, his father and other family members that she could not possibly know (some of the information I had to ask Gaurav's father to verify, which he did later). We spoke for half an hour or so and Gaurav, through her, filled me in on several events leading up to his death, some of which only his most trusted friends know and have kept as closely guarded secrets, and will continue to do so until the time is right.

Is this the final chapter of Gaurav Tiwari? I think not. Even in death, Gaurav is finding ways to connect with people and bring joy. This book may be the beginning of a renaissance (of sorts) of the teachings of Gaurav. It may also be another foundation stone in cementing his legacy in India and the rest of the world as a truly remarkable paranormal investigator and spiritual icon.

Vale Gaurav Tiwari.

AFTERLIFE COMMUNICATIONS

A brief write-up on the afterlife communications with my husband and the immense support received from Rev Gaurav Tiwari, Indian Paranormal Society

— DR NANDINI SINHA KAPUR

I was a simple working woman with a teaching job at a university. I was happy living a content life with my husband, Prof. Vijay Kapur, and my little son, Aditya. I never expected that my husband would pass away so suddenly, nor did I have much idea about the afterlife and the possibility of a genuine communication.

Vijay went to his office at the Faculty of Management Studies, University of Delhi on the morning of 31 May 2013. I got a phone call from his office at 2 p.m. that he had fallen unconscious and had been taken to a nearby hospital. I rushed there from my workplace. He was declared dead on arrival at the hospital, following a massive cardiac arrest. We were devastated. Too sudden. Not at all expected. I did not know how to handle this shocking personal loss along with bringing up my little son, who was exactly eight-and-a-half years old then. But

I got a strong sense of Vijay's presence around us from day one of his demise. There were signs. I could feel it. A number of unnatural occurrences seemed to be hinting at something too. When the body was yet to be cremated, his mobile phone kept showing different timings time and again. On the night of his chautha (fourth day after the funeral) ceremony, someone rang the doorbell several times, but there was nobody there when we went to check. On the way to Haridwar to immerse his ashes, I casually switched on and checked his phone. Someone had called the University of Delhi examination branch at 7.30 a.m. How could that be possible! The phone was with me all the time, and was switched off! It was also surprising as no government office really works at 7.30 in the morning. These were some sort of indications for sure that he wanted us to feel his presence.

More was yet to come. We kept hearing sounds like the drawing of curtains and utensils falling. I kept receiving blank messages from him on my mobile phone, and when I checked my late husband's outbox, there was no message. Then, I saw him!

28 September 2013. It had been a few days since Aditya had suffered a hairline fracture and was on bedrest. I was worried, and to make it worse, alone. I cried. I worried. I cried more. I worried more. One late night, I saw an apparition in my bedroom. It was him, I could make out. Aditya was fine within a week. Perhaps Vijay had come to assure me that our son would be okay. He wanted to tell us that he was still there, watching over us.

It was at this juncture that Rev Gaurav Tiwari came into my life. I was frantically looking for someone really educated in afterlife studies and communication as we had understood by now that Vijay was trying hard to contact us, especially me. I searched for organisations on the internet and finally found out about the Indian Paranormal Society, which had its office in Dwarka, New Delhi. Rev Gaurav Tiwari was shooting for *Haunting: Australia* in August 2013. I met him with great expectations in his office in mid-September. Gaurav bhai (he used to call me 'didi') was convinced like me that Vijay was keen to communicate with me after his death. All those sounds were his 'energies', he told me.

Gaurav taught me how to speak to Vijay and introduced the concept of Electronic Voice Phenomenon and instrumental trans-communication to me. I shall forever be grateful to Gaurav bhai for renewing my journey with my husband again. He encouraged me to go for voice recordings with Vijay and presented me with a simple voice recorder. So the first voice recorder in my life was a gift from Gaurav bhai. With great enthusiasm, I started recording sessions with Vijay quite frequently. Initially, I could not interpret the voices. I remember that I rushed to Gaurav with the first few recordings. When he replayed those recordings and read out aloud Vijay's words like 'hello' and 'love you', my joy knew no bounds. Gaurav trained me to speak to my husband in the spirit world.

Gradually, the EVPs yielded very good results, with Vijay speaking so many words like 'don't you worry', 'life and death', 'your Maa', 'Nandini', 'Adi', 'I am getting it better', 'eternal', 'God bless', 'good morning', and many such phrases. At times, he used to speak a full sentence (although in a low pitch). I would visit Gaurav once every month with my recordings and he used to analyse them with great enthusiasm.

Once, on a lighter note, he jokingly said that his computer had crashed with the volume of Vijay's EVPs.

Gaurav was very happy when I was awarded a small research grant by the Society for Psychic Research, London on the strength of my EVP recordings under the category of Survival Research. I went a step further with his help and he taught me water ITC, i.e. Instrumental TransCommunication (how to shoot photos of spirits with the help of water). We achieved great success in this as I was lucky to capture a photo of Vijay on 5 July 2015. Gaurav was thrilled to see it! It was he who brought out my story to the world. He arranged for a short documentary to be made on my story by Shweta Singh, one of the chief editors of Aaj Tak. She came to my house and shot this short film. It was telecast on 30 January 2016 under the prime time serial *Adbhut, Avishvasniya, Akalpaniya*.

I invited Gaurav for a lecture at my university on 15 January 2016. He spoke on ESP (Extra Sensory Phenomena), such was the bond with Rev Gaurav Tiwari— my bhai who enabled me to communicate with my late husband. What is most rewarding is that I continue to hear about him from my husband through psychography, i.e. automatic writing. Vijay has met him in the afterlife and, believe it or not, mentions that both of them are engaged in research on communication after death. They exist. The afterlife is real.

GLOSSARY

Anomaly: Something that is abnormal, peculiar or not easily classified. Anomalies are a part of the documentation/recordings done by paranormal researchers.

Apportion: A phenomena where objects are displaced or moved or disappear from where they were last seen or placed.

Asportion: A phenomena where objects are found or re-appear after being displaced from their original location.

Astral projection: Similar to an out-of-body experience. It is believed to be experienced by individuals with much practice of the art wherein the subject can intentionally separate their consciousness/spirit/soul from their physical body.

Attachment: A phenomena where a spirit/ghost attaches itself to a person. The subject may experience activities around him/her due to this attachment. Paranormal researchers also believe that attachment precedes a possession.

Cleansing: It is an activity performed by paranormal researchers/spiritual healers to help a client rid a place of unwanted energies or to help human agents rid themselves of any kind of attachment/possession. There are different techniques that are used by researchers/healers to perform the cleansing.

Devil/Inhuman entities: These are types of entities that are believed to not have experienced life in the way we humans have. They are believed to be evil/negative and their only purpose is to disrupt the lives of other beings.

Digital audio recorder (EVP recorder): Audio recording equipment used to document Electronic Voice Phenomena (EVP) and audio anomalies.

Echovox: An Instrumental TransCommunication Software used by paranormal researchers to communicate with spirits/ghosts/energies on a real-time basis. The software runs on an Apple/Android device and has a sound bank with pre-fed sounds, noises, words, etc. The ghosts/spirits are believed to manipulate these sounds that are randomly selected and played by the software to form a word that may or may not make sense to the paranormal researcher.

EMF: Electromagnetic frequency or electromagnetic fields that travel through space carrying electromagnetic radiant energy. They include radio waves, microwaves, infrared, light, ultraviolet, X-rays and gamma rays. They are commonly sourced from household electric equipment/ mobile phones/walkie-talkies, etc. Paranormal researchers usually document changes in electromagnetic fields when all household equipment is turned off and the ambient environment is void of radiations sourced from the above-mentioned devices.

EMF/K-II Meter: These are specialised equipment that help document and measure EMF fields that may be sourced by household equipment/devices/walkie-talkies/ mobile towers/unknown sources like ghosts/spirits/ energies. They are also used in industries to check for any electrical leakages in machinery and other equipment.

Entity: An 'entity' is defined by paranormal researchers as any haunting that shows some semblance of a living being (it could be in terms of shape, sound or any other way/ interaction).

EVP: Electronic Voice Phenomena are sounds documented on digital audio or analogue voice recorders believed to be sourced by ghosts/spirits/entities, etc. The documentation of this anomaly or sound is called an EVP.

Full spectrum camera: Cameras (photograph plus video) that are used by paranormal researchers to document in the night without an external light source. They are specialised pieces of equipment that capture pictures using broadband/ full-spectrum film which is visible and near-infrared light, commonly referred to as 'VNIR'. The human eyes can only see in a particular spectrum of light; however, a full spectrum camera possesses the ability to document in any and every spectrum of light ranging from infrared to ultraviolet.

Ghost: A 'ghost' is defined by paranormal researchers as an entity that resembles a human.

Haunting: The act of something or someone repeatedly visiting a place, thought or memory. Something that recurs persistently, disturbing the normal pattern of life, a reported activity that could be paranormal.

Hotspots: Places where most of the paranormal activities in an area are focused towards. These are spots that are marked by paranormal researchers to record anomalous activities using their equipment.

Intelligent haunting: It is a type of haunting where the presence communicates or responds in a way which correlates to something of significance to the paranormal researcher/subject of research/place.

Night vision camera: Also known as Infrared Camera, these are camera/photographic/video documentation devices used by paranormal researchers to capture anomalies in the night without an external light source. Infrared light is electromagnetic radiation (EMR) that has wavelengths longer than those of visible light and which therefore cannot be seen by the human eye.

Near death experience (NDE): An unusual experience where a person is on the brink of death (at times declared clinically dead by medical professionals) but returns to life with varied memories of what happened in the duration of being declared dead and coming back to life. Medical professionals have a different outlook on this experience, whereas paranormal researchers believe it is similar to an out-of-body experience.

Object manipulation: A phenomena where objects move on their own without a human agent interfering with it. It is believed that ghosts/spirits can psychokinetically move objects.

Out-of-body experience (OBE): It is a sensation/experience of being outside one's own body similar to floating or flying and at the same time being able to observe themselves (biological body) from a distance.

Paranormal investigation: A process during which investigators research and collect evidence in a place that is supposedly haunted. Documentation of changes in the ambient environment is a critical part of a paranormal investigation. These documentations sometimes include anomalies which may (after intensive analysis) turn into potential evidence that shares a strong link to the paranormal.

Past life regression (PLR): A method whereby a PLR practitioner uses hypnosis or similar techniques to tap into the subject's subconscious mind which they believe holds memories of their past life. It is also used as an alternative healing technique to relieve the subject of trauma.

Poltergeist: The term originates from a German word— 'polter' meaning 'noisy' and 'geist' meaning 'ghost'. It is believed to be a type of spirit/ghost that is responsible for physical disturbances such as loud noises and objects being moved or destroyed.

Possession: In layman terms, it means a subject being under the influence of something that results in a change of behaviour and overall personality. In paranormal research terms, researchers believe that some spirits/ghosts can influence people/subjects.

Residual haunting: It is based on the Stone Tape theory which says that impressions during a traumatic event can be 'recorded' on environmental elements like rocks or places. It is believed that emotional energy or memories can be captured within a space and may replay the event over and over again under certain conditions.

Sage: A herb that is one of the oldest and purest methods of cleansing a person and space, and getting rid of unwanted energies.

Soul: A soul is defined by paranormal researchers as an interactive intelligent human haunting.

Spirit: A spirit is defined by paranormal researchers as the ghost of a once-living person that contains non-physical attributes like emotion and personality.

Survival hypothesis: It is a hypothesis based on the belief that we humans live via the emotions that we experience, and that our physical body without the mind acts like a non-living object. It reinforces the belief that human consciousness (awareness, intelligence, mind, thoughts, emotions and overall personality) can withstand physical death.

Tibetan/Buddhist singing bowl: A bowl that, when stroked with a mallet, produces a rich, deep tone. The effects of the vibrations and sounds are believed to be cleansing.

Tri-field meter: Also known as a tri-Axis field meter is an EMF measuring device that has a three-axis sensor. It is a single unit that combines all the features needed for fast, accurate measurements of electromagnetic fields and radio frequencies.